THE COURT FACTOR

Alfred Apsler is also the author of:

THE TIES BETWEEN: A CENTURY OF JUDAISM
ON AMERICA'S LAST FRONTIER
(in collaboration with Rabbi Julius J. Nodel)

NORTHWEST PIONEER (a Covenant Book)

FIGHTER FOR INDEPENDENCE: Jawaharlal Nehru

THE COURT FACTOR:

The Story of
Samson Wertheimer

by Alfred Apsler

illustrated by Albert Gold

The Jewish Publication Society of America

5724-1964   Philadelphia

FIRST PRINTING 1964

Copyright © 1964 by The Jewish Publication Society of America
All rights reserved
Library of Congress catalog card number: 64-16755
Manufactured in the United States of America by
The Haddon Craftsmen, Inc.
Designed by Albert Gold

Introductory Note

Samson Wertheimer (1658-1724) was one of the most interesting personalities of pre-modern times. The most successful businessman of his day and financial advisor to emperors and princes, he was also a student of the Talmud and the official Chief Rabbi of Hungary. He wrote books and preached sermons and at all times defended the Jewish people against the many dangers that faced them.

Samson Wertheimer was born into a scholarly family and therefore was sent to a *yeshiva* to obtain a good talmudic education. He married into the family of the famous Samuel Oppenheimer, whom he eventually succeeded as administrator of the finances of the Imperial Court of Vienna. Wertheimer was more successful than his uncle by marriage, probably because of his greater tact in dealing with the proud grandees of the time. The German and Austrian nobles heaped honors upon him; they referred to him as "The Jewish Emperor."

War was constant in those days, yet no government had what we now call a Quartermaster Corps, or even a finance department for its army. Such matters as supplying the armies' needs or paying the soldiers, all of whom were mercenaries, were entrusted to private businessmen called Factors, whom the governments then repaid in lump sums. It was a very risky business, since a lost war meant bankruptcy for the Court Factor. Moreover, sometimes, when the sums due to the Factor grew to vast size, the reigning monarchs could easily accuse their Factors of dishonesty and refuse to pay. You could not easily summon the Emperor to a lawsuit. This is what happened to Samuel Oppenheimer and to other Court Factors. One can see, therefore, what a dangerous life Samson Wertheimer lived and how remarkably wise he was in his relations with the dukes, kings and emperors whom he served.

A good book to read on the subject of the Court Factors is one written by Selma Stern entitled *The Court Jew*, published by the Jewish Publication Society in 1950.

Chapter **1**

"Stop that whistling, Samson. As if the bumping coach were not enough punishment for me."

A loud burst of laughter preceded the answer:

"So you don't appreciate my tunes. Well, Nathan, trouble with you is you take things too hard. Sing, whistle, joke with the people you meet, and you won't have time to think of your queasy stomach."

The laughing brown-haired youth slapped his companion heartily on the shoulder. Nathan shuddered at the touch. Before he could give an angry answer the coach in which they were traveling tilted dangerously. One wheel had slid into a chuckhole. The whole clumsy vehicle groaned as it righted itself. Nathan's face turned several shades greener.

"That confounded coachman." Rapping with his fist against the front wall he shouted weakly, "Hey, Veit, can't you lead the horses 'round the holes? You'll wreck the coach and break all our necks. I told you not to drink so much at the last inn."

3

Samson chuckled.

"Might as well save your breath. Old Veit's taking his nap. The horses know their way."

"Say, what are you so happy about? We've suffered in this rolling cage for more'n a week. And besides, for a Yeshiva student you're behaving quite strangely—singing at the inn with the peasants, whistling dance tunes—pooh."

"All right, you stop complaining, and I'll put my dignity back on."

For a while they sat facing each other in silence. Nathan pressed himself into the corner, his frail body shaken by nervous spasms, while Samson gazed out over the rolling fields and the little straw-thatched farm houses.

It was an early summer afternoon in 1675. The air was fragrant with the scent of apple and peach blossoms, and through the cloud of dust churned up by the wheels the travelers could see peasants cutting the first hay with their long scythes. The neat yellow strips of farm land were framed by the dark forest in the distance.

The two young men were returning to their homes in Worms on the Rhine from the Cracow Yeshiva, where they had been sent to study Talmud. Young German Jews destined for the rabbinate often went to Poland because there they could study under the most famous talmudic scholars.

The pale thin face of Nathan Oppenheimer fitted the black round-brimmed hat which, together with the long black cloak, was the garb of his future profession. But though his eighteen year-old cousin Samson Wertheimer wore similar clothes, he seemed to belong to a different world. His healthy red cheeks did not betray long months spent in dusty study rooms over yellowed folios.

As Samson watched the peaceful German landscape roll by, he thoughtfully pulled his left earlock, which dangled down to his neck. He was not very tall, but his shoulders were broad, and his gray eyes reflected curiosity and determination.

With a grimace of discomfort Nathan raised himself from his corner. The cushion he had placed behind his back rolled to the floor. He glanced out at the sun that rode herd on a gay flock of cumulus clouds in the otherwise spotless sky.

A slight shade of color showed in his face. "Time for afternoon prayer." The prospect of an interruption brought vigor into his voice. "Veit, stop the horses."

He pounded and pounded till the coachman was finally aroused. The team was brought to a halt, and the two students stepped out into the light breeze and stretched their cramped limbs. Nathan's lips almost formed a thin smile as they walked slowly along the briar hedge that separated the road from the fields.

Under a cluster of birches whose white trunks contrasted pleasantly with the massed green of the leaves, they stopped. They turned to the east, the direction from which they had come, and with their bodies slightly swaying from the hips they went through the brief ritual of daily worship.

Nathan tried to walk as slowly as he possibly could

on their way back to the coach. "We must hurry," Samson reminded him. "The sun will be setting soon, and it's still far to the next town."

With a deep sigh Nathan walked the last steps. He entered the coach reluctantly, as if it were a torture chamber.

The gate to the walled town of Langen was still open, for the sun could still be seen above the horizon. Outside the gatekeeper's shack sat a group of men throwing dice on an upended barrel. A nearly empty flask of red wine rested on the cobblestones. It must have been passed around many times, for their faces were flushed and their voices loud and hoarse. The players were young men except for the gatekeeper himself, a grizzled peg-legged veteran of some war.

Sulkily, he looked up from the game at the peasant wagons returning from the fields through the gate.

"Won't get any toll out o'those beggars," he grumbled. "Well, time t'lock up for the night."

Painfully he heaved himself up from the block of firewood on which he had been sitting.

Then a spark of alertness came into his reddened eyes as he looked down the two lines of hedgerows that bordered the road.

"What d'ya know," he mumbled. "A late customer. It's the first travel coach coming to town all day. No wonder merchants 're scared to travel. What with all those eternal wars. First it's the Protestants against the Catholics an' now the Frenchmen arguing with the

Emperor. An' me sittin' here all day without collectin' a single penny in toll."

"Let's go an' have a look," bellowed a young blond giant. "An' you, Hannes, stop gripin'. We bought your wine, anyhow."

The ivory cubes dropped from his big hands as he stood up. His companions followed.

The coach halted before the gate. The two cousins stepped down and waited for the slowly approaching gatekeeper. At the sight of the travelers' clothes the big diceplayer let out a low whistle. He gave his friends an ugly wink which meant, "Come on, let's have some fun with 'em." The whole group advanced.

The gatekeeper's voice grated harshly. "No strange Jews allowed here." His disappointment over losing the unexpected toll money made it sound doubly harsh.

But then his face brightened, and his big red nose shone with pleasure. Nathan had pulled from the folds of his cloak a parchment scroll with a large seal dangling from it on a string. It was that special passport issued by the Bishop of Worms which granted free movement to a few privileged Jews and their families. At the same time Samson stretched out his hand, in which sparkled a big silver coin.

The gatekeeper was satisfied. The coin was bright and heavy. But the big blond fellow stepped closer.

"You think they got some more of that stolen money under their filthy black rags?" he shouted to his companions. They smacked their lips in anticipation.

The gatekeeper was nowhere to be seen. He had scurried back into his shack with the silver coin.

Nathan, his face an ashen gray, shrank back towards the coach and fumbled for the door handle.

"Look." Their tormentor pointed at him. "Sneaky cowards, all o' em. Ever seen a Jew who'd stand up an' fight like a man?" He spat on the ground and wiped his mouth on a dirty sleeve.

"You're seeing one now, and I hope you'll remember him, you drunken bully."

The words rang out sharply like shots from a musket. At the same time a fist smashed into the dice player's perspiring face and sent him reeling back into the knot of men. Samson stood erect, panting. He seemed to have grown taller suddenly. His right hand was still clenched into a tight fist while his left tugged nervously at the sidelock.

"Why, you vermin, you . . . you—" The town tough was so surprised at this response to his taunts that he could not find words. Five fists were raised, and five pairs of feet shuffled closer to the carriage.

Nathan was a picture of deathly fright. Desperately he pulled at his cousin's sleeve to draw him into the coach. But Samson shook him off with one angry shrug.

"Back everybody," hissed the rowdy. "This Jew boy's mine. Watch me kill 'im."

"Go on, finish 'im off, Klaus," shouted the others as they formed a jagged circle around the attacker and his victim.

The man called Klaus crouched like a beast of prey

for the fatal leap. In the next instant the fighters were rolling on the ground, a ball of flesh wildly kicking and pulling. The onlookers roared and stomped their feet in wild excitement.

Then Samson was on his feet again. Blood trickled from his nose and oozed from one corner of his mouth. His cloak had a long rip and was smeared with dust. One eye had turned an ugly purple where his foe had landed a solid blow. But with the agility of a snake he avoided more direct hits.

The enemy's huge left hand grabbed Samson's cloak tightly at the breast to set him up for another blow. For a moment his right fist was suspended in mid-air.

"Give it to 'im, good and hard," screamed one of his friends. Breathlessly, they waited for the end.

But with lightning speed Samson dropped to his knees, twisting himself out of the other's grasp. At the same time he pulled one of Klaus' legs from under him. With a dull crash the big man went down. Samson leaped. He was on top of him with a strangle-hold.

"Had enough?" he gasped as his thumbs dug cruelly into his opponent's jugular veins. Klaus twisted and squirmed, his eyes protruding from their sockets. "Enough." His breath came in painful spurts. "You win."

Immediately Samson jumped to his feet. Without giving the crowd another glance he turned and mounted the carriage. "Come, Nathan," he said to his trembling cousin. "Didn't you say we'll stay with Reb Arnsteiner over night? It's getting late."

The coach creaked slowly through the gate. Then it picked up speed as it headed towards the center of town. The men stood open-mouthed. For a while nobody moved. The vanquished ruffian began to pick himself slowly and painfully up from the ground.

In front of Isaac Arnsteiner's narrow three-story house the street was empty. But at the corner, two blocks away, a crowd had formed and was staring silently in the direction of the house.

The big iron-studded door was closed. But as soon as the travelers had stepped out of the coach a few moments earlier, it had opened to a mere slit, and a hand had waved them frantically inside. Reb Arnsteiner, a short man with a wisp of gray beard, had peered anxiously up and down the street. Then he slammed the door shut. He shot a heavy bolt across and secured it with a clanking chain.

"Come, come. Don't stand here by the street. Get upstairs. A riot by my house—that's all I need."

So he knew already, thought Samson tugging again at his left sidelock. News certainly traveled fast in Langen.

"Sorry, Reb Arnsteiner, if we have frightened you. Of course, I didn't want this to happen, but—"

"Shush. It's done. What's the use regretting? Maybe it's all to the good. But just today it had to happen. Not enough trouble I have already."

What was he talking about? What other trouble?

Perhaps fright had made the elderly gentleman a little
giddy.

Nathan clutched his stomach. His face was wrinkled
with pain. The latest events had been too much for his
nerves.

"I think I'm going to be sick," he rasped, "if I can't
lie down quickly and rest."

"Poor Nate." His host led him to a darkened room.
"Over there is a couch. I'll drop in on you later. You're
a good fellow, a real student and not a troublemaker,
like—like some. Now you, Samson, come follow me."

They climbed narrow stairs and stepped into an attic
room which had sloping walls and a dormer towards the
street. In the dim light of a single candle, Samson saw
a man trying to lift a corner of the dormer curtain and
peer into the street. The noise of their entrance made
him spin around. His right hand reached swiftly inside
his loose blouse, a good hiding place for a knife.

"Relax, Regner. It's a friend of mine," said the merchant. "Or you think I'll tell the town constable on you?
You're safe here; that is, as long as we're safe ourselves."

He shot a reproachful glance at Samson and then
turned to the fugitive again:

"Regner, this is the son of Rabbi Isaac Wertheimer of
Worms. He is about to become a rabbi himself. He's
now returning home from his studies. But right now
—well, what's this all about anyhow, Sam? You were
in a fight with that drunken butcher boy Klaus? A
Talmud scholar fighting?"

Samson gave a brief account of the events at the

town gate. Arnsteiner's face became moist with perspiration. His voice shook slightly.

"Why, you young fool. Wrestling like a drunken peasant. An' you could've brought the whole town chasing after you an' breaking into my house. Good that my wife and children are out of town visiting my sister."

Then his frown changed to a smile. "Yet I would give a good silver thaler to see that Klaus' face. He had it coming."

"Young friend, let me shake your hand. It's a privilege to meet a brave man like you."

The stranger's hand shot out from the folds of his blouse, empty. Like a vise it gripped Samson's fingers.

"Thank you, Herr Regner. You're not a Jew, are you?"

"No," explained their host. "This is Gotthold Regner, my number one trouble. You're number two. O my poor head."

He pushed back the little skull cap and scratched his head.

"Now you tell 'im why you're here an' everything while I go an' make poor Nathan comfortable. Then I'll see about a bite to eat an' some hot tea."

The two young men were left alone. Immediately Regner let out a torrent of speech. Walking up and down in the tiny garret he bumped his head at every turn. His arms sailed through the air, and his right index finger pointed accusingly at invisible opponents.

He had studied for the Protestant ministry at Freiburg. But when he saw how little the princes and nobles lived up to the teachings of the Bible, he had felt compelled to speak out against them. He attacked them at the university, at students' inns, and also in a pamphlet which was being passed around among many students and citizens.

Regner was warming up to his favorite subject.

"Men are equal before God," he shouted. "Every man has a right to express himself according to his conscience. But the kings and the dukes and the bishops want to keep us in ignorance and superstition—"

"I see," interrupted Samson. Now he understood his host's fear. Regner's voice could surely be heard for two or three blocks. "And what happened to you? How come you're here?"

The Duke of Hesse had been mentioned in the pamphlet in very unflattering terms. So when the rebellious theologian appeared in Frankfort, the Duke had sent soldiers to arrest him at his inn. Gotthold escaped by a hair's breadth by jumping through a back window and stealing out of town. He had hiked all night till he reached Arnsteiner's house at dawn. The Jewish merchant was known to him as an honest friend of the poor and persecuted. For the moment Regner was safe, but he was still in the Duke's territory.

Pulling at his curled earlock, Samson was already devising a plan.

"You're coming with us tomorrow. If we can get you into Worms I can hide you and then show you an escape route to Holland."

"Ah, Holland. There's the sound of freedom and progress in that name. Yes, my friend, I'll go to Holland and raise my voice from there even louder—"

"Don't raise your voice in my house." The merchant was back, loaded down with bread, cheese, and a jug full of steaming brown liquid. "Here, take this. At least you can't shout while you're eating."

He deposited his load on a tiny table. "It's quiet outside, thank God. Tomorrow we'll have to get all of you out of here. Good night now."

Only now did Samson realize how hungry he was. Gotthold, too, showed a healthy appetite. In no time at all the tray was cleared of food.

"Now here is how we'll do it tomorrow." Samson took one last gulp and then pushed back the empty jug. Arnsteiner would dig up another black cloak and round hat for Gotthold. And so, instead of two, there would be three yeshiva students in the coach.

"What about the guards at the gate of Worms?"

"We have our letter of protection with the Bishop's seal. Those fellows cannot read, or at best only a few words. They'll be impressed by the seal and by a good-size silver piece. Just keep your eyes down and try to look humble. I know that won't be easy for you."

They both laughed.

The candle burned down to a tiny stump and finally went out. They bedded down on the floor and wrapped themselves in blankets.

Samson listened as his new friend told him about the stirring ideas that were occupying the minds of many scholars. They were restless, groping for a way to a better world. A new age was being born, prouder, happier, than any before.

Samson never knew how late the hour was when he finally fell into a deep sleep of exhaustion.

Chapter 2

It was early morning, and a light drizzle fell on the fields outside of Worms. The two young men walking along the narrow field path had the hoods of their cloaks drawn down over their foreheads. The few plowmen in sight did not pay them any attention, for they looked like two journeymen wandering from town to town—a very common sight.

On the crown of a hill they halted. Gotthold Regner dropped the bundle which he had been carrying on a stick over his shoulder. He was a little out of breath.

"This is quite a hike for one who spends his days bent over books. I wonder how you do it, Samson. You seem as calm and rested as after a little stroll to the town square."

"I like to take long walks. Have been doing it for years, almost every day."

Samson pointed into the distance, into a sea of low, rain-heavy clouds.

"Over there is the Rhine River. On a clear day you'd

see it. Just follow this path, and you'll get there some-
time in the afternoon. There's a little inn where the
bargemen stop. You'll easily get one to take you along
downstream, towards Holland. And don't forget—talk
only about the crops and the quality of the wine."

Warmly, they shook hands. For a moment Gotthold
Regner, the fiery orator, was at a loss for words.

"Thanks for everything," he said finally, "and I mean
not only your help. I have learned a great lesson. For the
first time I've stayed under a Jewish roof, and I found
what I long suspected that deep down, under their
different clothes, good men everywhere feel alike and
strive for the same goals."

"I think I've learned more than you, Gotthold. I've
learned that it's wrong for a Jew to see an enemy in
every outsider. I know now there's something brewing
in the minds of you students that will one day draw
us all closer together."

"Yes, one day rulers won't lead their men to the
slaughter-house anymore like so many sheep, and—"

"Yes, yes, Gotthold. We spoke about these things
practically all night while you were hiding in our cellar.
But now you better move along if you want to reach the
Rhine before nightfall."

"Farewell, brother. I have a feeling we'll see each
other again."

For a long time Samson stood on the hill and watched
Regner disappear in the mist. Then he began to re-
trace his steps back to the city.

It was past the noon hour when he returned to the

ghetto street of Worms. In the rain, the worn cobble-stones looked slick and polished. Under the arched stone arcades wares of all kinds were spread out on tables and in baskets. The smell of cooking drifted out of open doors, and through the windows of the ancient synagogue came the sing-song of children's voices reciting Hebrew sentences in unison.

In all honesty Samson had to admit to himself that he was tired now. He leaned against one of the pillars that supported the arcades. His eyes were closed, and he felt drowsiness creep up from his limbs into his brain.

Inside him was a gnawing emptiness. What lay ahead? To be his father's assistant, to study intricate com-mentaries on Scripture, perhaps to write one of his own? Was that what he wanted? It seemed to be leading nowhere.

Through his mind flashed an ugly picture: the hood-lum in Langen, his face full of hatred and contempt. And then he thought of Gotthold's dream: a new world of free, enlightened men without ghettoes.

No, he was not ready for the pulpit and the study room. Unconsciously, Samson shook himself as if to throw off invisible webs that tied and strangled him. Passers-by looked at him in surprise.

Somewhere in this world the great adventure was waiting. But where was it? Where was the key to it?

He did not know how long he had been leaning against the pillar day-dreaming. Suddenly he stumbled. People were pushing him as they rushed by. Down the street he saw a rapidly growing crowd, right in front of the house where Nathan's family lived.

Automatically Samson followed the throng. In the middle of the street, blocking passage, stood a magnificent carriage with four snorting bay horses. A footman, liveried in blue and silver, had jumped from his high seat. He let down the footsteps and threw open the door.

Three people stepped out.

First there appeared a portly man dressed in the latest fashion: a velvet frock coat over a white ruffled silk shirt, silk breeches, a powdered wig, and a three-cornered hat with a big diamond-studded clasp.

"It's Samuel Oppenheimer," Samson heard an excited woman whisper to another.

So this was the great Samuel Oppenheimer, the "Court Jew." Samson had heard of him. In fact, he could claim a distant relationship, since Oppenheimer was Nathan's uncle. But the famous master of high finance had not been to Worms in years, at least not as long as Samson could remember. Yet he owned the house into which he was now being conducted by Nathan and his father, who were flustered and nervous.

Samson tried to recall the tales that went around the ghettoes about the Jew who served royalty and shared the glitter of their lives. Samuel Oppenheimer loaned money to the Duke of Lorraine to build a new palace, procured muskets and ammunition for the Margrave of Baden, horses and fodder for the Elector Palatine, paintings and rare books for the Archbishops of Mayence and

Treves. Even the Emperor in Vienna depended on him for quick credit when he wanted to outfit an army or bribe the minister of a hostile country.

Officially Oppenheimer was called a "court factor," which could mean almost anything and often did. He acted as finance minister, tax collector, banker, quartermaster general, and confidential diplomatic courier for various petty princes of the German Empire. They could always rely on the Court Jew, while their own nobles were often rebellious and disdained any hard work except fighting.

Enthusiastic well-wishers surrounded the wealthy visitor. Hands were stretched out to him from all sides. He was visibly pleased and acknowledged the loud greetings with a broad smile.

Hardly anyone noticed the second passenger who left the carriage. But Samson's heart skipped a beat as he looked for a split-second into deep brown eyes that swept the scene with an air of sadness and loneliness. The girl's face appeared small and dainty under the large silken shawl that hung down over her dark gray travel coat. Her skin had the smoothness of mother-of-pearl.

Now the third arrival alighted from the carriage. He was still a young man, but his body was bent and emaciated. "A ghost," thought Samson. A ghost with deep-set burning eyes that did not see the street before them, but stared into a hidden world. Samson felt a cold shiver run down his spine.

In the next moment he was looking at the girl again. She paused at the door, her back turned to him. It was a graceful slender back. Lifting the trailing hem of her cloak, she followed the Court Factor into the house.

Everybody was pressing after them. Samson gave in to the pressure that swept him into the parlor room of the Oppenheimer residence.

Samuel Oppenheimer was holding court, flanked by his relatives. The poor had come to flatter him, hoping he would, as often happened, display his widely famed generosity. And then there were the well-to-do leaders of the ghetto, many of whom were Oppenheimer's correspondents and sub-contractors. They depended on him for their livelihood and shared his risks. Now they were making their reports and receiving new instructions.

Finally it was Samson's turn to present himself.

"Why, it's Rabbi Wertheimer's son." The Court Factor was in a gay mood. He was pleased with the reception, pleased to be the pride and envy of his people. "Last time I saw you, you were sitting on my lap. Frumet, step closer," he called to his lovely travel companion who stood with Nathan's mother and sister in a far corner. "This is Samson Wertheimer who has been to the Yeshiva with Nathan."

The girl blushed, and Samson stumbled over his own legs as he went to grasp her outstretched hand. With an encouraging smile she looked at the embarrassed youth, but her smiling mouth still betrayed a trace of sadness.

"I have heard from Nathan that you are quite a scholar." Her voice was the sweetest music he had ever heard.

He mumbled something in return. It was meant to be

a modest denial, but he was sure she could not possibly
have understood him. Fortunately, the older woman
now took her arm, "Come, Frumet. You're exhausted
and starving. We'll take you to your room."

The parlor remained crowded all afternoon. There
was a constant coming and going. Samson had no good
reason to stay, yet he could not bring himself to leave.
Nobody paid any attention to him.

Hours passed. Suddenly, he saw the pale stranger
again. He emerged from one of the back rooms and made
straight for the door. His eyes, shaded by a black fur-
trimmed hat, seemed to have retreated even deeper into
their sockets. Without so much as a glance at the as-
sembled crowd, he stepped out into the street.

To his astonishment Samson watched Frumet rush
by and follow him. She had changed into a lighter gown,
fashionably cut in front to show her white bodice. Instead of a travel shawl, she now wore a small bonnet
which allowed her rich black tresses to fall on her
shoulders.

The men in the parlor fell silent and stared after the
stranger. Several also turned to follow.

Samson fell in with the little procession. Heading for
the synagogue, it grew in size with every step.

"It's Judah Chassid," he heard a man call to another
who stood under the arcade. "He'll speak after evening
prayer."

"The Cabbalist? He's here in Worms? Wait a moment
while I close the shop."

By the time Samson squeezed himself into the half-

darkened prayer hall, the pews were filled. Men of all
ages stood tightly packed against the walls. Even the
women's section behind the screen buzzed excitedly,
although it was only an ordinary weekday.

The old cantor began to chant the service. A tingling
air of expectancy filled the hall. The prayers were whispered in hurried subdued tones. Then, after the last
"amen," the whole assembly lapsed into a tense silence.

Again Samson felt that chill running up and down
his spine. He saw Judah Chassid stand up, kiss the gold-
embroidered velvet curtain of the Ark, and then turn
to face the people who sat with their bodies bent forward. His eyes seemed to bore right through each listener.

"Friends, I have come to warn you," he began with
a shrill, piercing voice. "The day of the Messiah is at
hand. I have studied the holy signs, the letters in the
Torah that have a hidden meaning known only to few
men. The signs speak loudly. Deliverance is almost here."

A rustle of awe swept through the hall like the first
swell that announces the storm. Sounds of weeping
came from the women's section.

The mystic messenger paused. He stretched out his
thin arm, and the listeners shrank back in terror as he
pointed a long bony finger at them.

"Woe unto those who will be found wanting on the
day the Lord sends his Messiah. They will be buried in
their houses of suffering. They will fall under the swords
of the heathen. But those who repent will follow him
eastward, to the holy city of Jerusalem—"

A deep sigh swept through the gathering. "Jerusalem,"

cried an old man. He jumped to his feet shaking grotesquely. Others followed his example. Their bodies swayed. Indecipherable shouts came from their lips.

"He will lead us up the mountain." The speaker's face was turned heavenward. He had forgotten where he was. He was alone with his vision. "And there he will erect again the Temple as in the days of Solomon. From the River Sambation will come marching the Ten Lost Tribes, a proud army with shining weapons. They will welcome their brethren who are now poor and hungry and despised. But nobody will be poor when the Messiah comes. The children of Israel will be a nation of princes—"

Samson was determined to fight the magic spell that had bound everyone else. He felt his pulse beat violently against his temples. Suddenly he turned to reach the door. He stepped on tapping feet and knocked against trembling shins.

Panting, he stood in the little courtyard which led into the synagogue. It was almost dark now, and a big unreal moon hung like a giant yellow lantern above the tall houses of the ghetto.

Never had he seen the people in such a state of rapture. He knew most of them: quiet, hard-working traders and craftsmen. And now, a few words from a roving Cabbalist, and they became dreamers walking in fairyland.

He had heard of this movement before. To the study halls of the Yeshiva had come rumors from far away. In Turkey, a man had proclaimed himself the Messiah.

Untold thousands were saluting him with outbreaks of indescribable joy. But they were ignorant, said Samson's teachers. The man was certainly a swindler.

Now he saw his own neighbors ignited by this mysterious fire.

He knew that his father had often preached against it, calling it a horror in the eyes of God. That was why Rabbi Wertheimer had stayed away this evening. He disapproved, yet he was powerless.

Uncomfortably, Samson pulled his left earlock. Who was right? His father, who said that only the study of the Talmud was pleasing to God, or those seers with their secret letters and signs? How was he to know?

His sweat-soaked clothes clung to his body. He shivered in the chill of the evening air.

The meeting was over. The people streamed out of the synagogue in silence. They walked with springy steps, still enveloped in the great dream.

Then came Frumet, all alone. The other women of the Oppenheimer household were probably still caught inside in the crush.

Following an impulse, Samson found himself beside her. They were walking together down the street. On this evening they were not aware that they were breaking the rules of proper behavior.

Neither of them spoke till they were almost at the Oppenheimer house.

"It's great to be alive in these days," said the girl finally.

"Do you really believe all that about the Messiah

arriving now any day, about all Jews leaving and going to the land of Israel?"

"I believe it. We must believe it. It's the only hope. Don't you?"

For the first time she turned her head sideways to look at him with big, surprised eyes.

"Lots of scholars are against Judah Chassid's ideas. My father, for example."

"He will change his mind. He will believe some day, and so will you, Samson."

So she remembered his name. He felt very good about it.

They had arrived at the door.

"Don't go yet," he pleaded. "Let's talk some more about it. I'm so confused by all this."

"You know already how I feel."

"I wish I had everything clearly figured out as you have. Perhaps if we could talk it over together—"

Suddenly frightened, she turned toward the door. What was she doing standing with this boy here in the street where everybody was walking by? How foolish of her.

"No, Samson, I'm sorry. I shouldn't have—. It's just that this meeting upset me so. I must go now. Nathan is waiting for me inside."

"Nathan Oppenheimer? Why is he waiting for you?"

He did not like the idea at all: Nathan being with her when he, Samson, could not.

"Don't you know yet? He is my fiancé. Uncle Samuel has arranged the engagement."

"Engagement?" he stammered. "You want him for a husband?"

"Want him? Don't be foolish. I saw him only once before today when we were little children. But that's the way things are done. My parents in Mannheim have given their consent. So it's all settled."

Samson was a picture of utter bewilderment. For a moment Frumet's eyes looked deeply and sadly into his. Then she was gone, lost in the darkness of the doorway.

For some time Samson stood as if struck by a hard blow. Then a hand tapped his shoulder.

"So, it's the Rabbi's son. What're you doing here? Your house is on the other end of the street by the synagogue."

It was the Court Factor himself who had stepped out of the house.

"I—I was just walking."

"I think I saw from the window with whom you were walking. Remember that she's engaged to another man and that you're a future rabbi."

"I remember."

He swallowed hard. Then a thought struck him.

"Actually I was waiting for you, Reb Samuel."

"For me? I would never have guessed. What about?"

"I want to enter your services. Could you use an apprentice clerk?"

"Well, that's a surprise. I thought you were all set to become a great talmudist. And your father? He expects you to be his successor, doesn't he?"

"I'll never make a good rabbi. I must do things, not just study about them. I want to know what it's like to be rich and powerful."

"Rich and powerful, eh? And overnight too? You think it's a bed of roses I'm lying on. Perhaps it's a good idea to let you find out for yourself. And besides, it'll take your mind off certain matters."

"So you'll take me?"

"Yes. Go an' talk with your father. I must leave tomorrow. Join me in Heidelberg as soon as you can. But mind you, it'll be hard work."

"All right, Reb Samuel, and thanks. I'll be in Heidelberg soon."

Chapter **3**

The road to Heidelberg ran by terraced vineyards that stretched for miles along the banks of the Neckar River. From steep cliffs the ruined walls and turrets of medieval castles greeted travelers. Samson looked up and wondered whether the ghosts of knights-in-armor were still walking the crenelated bastions on dark nights. Or did wretched prisoners still clank their chains deep down in the dungeons?

Then, swinging his bundle gaily with the rhythm of his steps, he turned his thoughts back to the present, and out into the future.

Wasn't he on his way to seek his fortune? And his fortune waited at the end of the road, in Heidelberg.

His forehead wrinkled into a determined frown. Yes, he was going to show all of them. One day he would do as he pleased, and nobody would dare stand in his way.

Once and for all he would be rid of Jew tolls and Jew streets. They would bow before him instead of calling him ugly names. And his own people? How they would stare at him! He would teach them that a Jew can rise as high as anybody, if he sets his mind to it.

There was his father. It had been painful to tell him that he felt no urge to be a rabbi. Isaac Wertheimer never expected that his children would oppose his will.

He would never forget the look of deep pain on his father's face as he turned to walk out of the study, a defiant son.

Wrapped in thought, Samson stumbled straight into a flock of geese that waddled, chattering, across the road. With angry squawks of protest they closed ranks again behind him.

That evening he would be in Heidelberg with his new employer, proud, strutting Samuel Oppenheimer. "He acts as if he were sitting on top of the world," thought Samson.

He bit his lips, and ground his teeth. "I'll beat him at his own game yet. I'll stay with him only long enough to learn his tricks. Then we'll be competitors. It'll be a rough fight, and may the better man win."

On the opposite bank of the Neckar the bell of a village church pealed softly. The sound reminded Samson of Frumet's voice, a gentle voice full of longing and hope.

Frumet was gone. Mannheim was not very far from here, but it might as well have been on the other side of the earth. In a few days she would stand under the wedding canopy with Nathan, the frail bookworm.

Samson broke into an angry trot. As he ran, dust rose

from the deep ruts and settled on his linen peasant blouse.

If he had watched the road ahead instead of staring grimly into space he would have noticed several men squatting on the grass under an old linden tree. As he came closer, they jumped up and barred his way. Two of them leaned against the long barrels of muskets while the others held pikes in their hands.

"Hey, lad," growled a ragged soldier with a drooping mustache. "Not so fast. You're carrying too much of a load. Just drop that bundle an' also that coin bag you've in your belt. Take off your shoes. Then you can march along. Barefoot walking is good for yer health."

"What's this?" Shocked back into reality Samson halted, then moved a step backward. "Who are you? A band of highwaymen?"

"Never mind the talk. Just do as I say. We're soldiers of the Margrave of Baden an' we know how to handle these little tools."

While his left hand supported the musket, his right whipped out a vicious curved dagger. He held it so close to Samson that its point touched his throat.

"But—but—" Even the nasty gleam of the metal right under his nose could not quiet his anger. "I'm not an enemy. You're fighting the French, aren't you? This is the Margrave's own land."

Another soldier, an older man with graying whiskers and a kind twinkle in his eyes, tapped him on the shoulder. "Calm yourself, young fellow. I'm not enjoying this. We can't fight Frenchmen on an empty stomach.

Haven't been paid for the last six months. Not even the filthiest innkeeper will give us credit anymore."

"Enough o'this," hissed the man with the dagger. "Drop that bundle or—"

Samson felt the blood welling up in the back of his head. His temples throbbed. His vision was blurred, and the soldier in front suddenly exchanged features with the brute who had taunted him at the Langen town gate.

Uttering an inarticulate scream of rage, he ducked quickly, and his fist plunged into the soldier's stomach. The dagger clattered to the ground, and the man sat down heavily, with a very surprised look on his broad face.

But this time the odds against Samson were too heavy. At one jump the whole pack was on him. He kicked and clawed, but it was no use. He lay pinned to the ground, and the heavy-set men were putting painful pressure on his arms and legs. Tears of helpless rage streaked his dust-caked cheeks.

The soldier whom he had struck tucked the dagger back into his belt. Grimly, he brought his musket into position, resting it on its forked support. He rammed the charge down the barrel and then swung it towards its target.

"Stand back, comrades," he shouted into the commotion, "so I can finish off that rascal."

"Sorry, my boy," murmured the older man before he stepped aside. "That was foolish o'you, but brave. You'd make a good soldier. Hey, Sepp." He turned to the waiting musketeer. "Give the poor devil time for a last prayer. We can wait that long, for sure."

A strong oath was the answer, but the musket barrel was lowered.

Then Samson heard the clatter of hoofs. Shouts of dismay came from the group of soldiers. The hands that had held him were gone, and so was the blue-black barrel of the weapon. He jumped up and tried to shake the sticky clods of mud from his clothes.

"You thieving rabble," bellowed a mighty bass. "Doin' your sport with the peasants again, eh? Can't you behave like soldiers?"

"It's not that we like to do it, Yer Highness," Samson heard his bewhiskered friend say. "But we haven't had a real meal for days and not a single copper in the pocket."

He was talking to a big man on a powerful snorting horse. A long traveling cape hid his clothing, but his high leather leggings, clanking silver spurs, and the long sword that slapped against the charger's side suggested nobility and high military rank.

A large retinue of riders with extra packhorses had stopped at a respectful distance.

"Who's the lad?" asked the commander. "Is he from the village over there?"

His well-groomed black goatee quivered as he spoke.

"Your lucky day," whispered the bewhiskered soldier as he nudged Samson forward. "It's our general, Margrave Louis of Baden himself."

"My name is Samson Wertheimer, sire, and I am on

my way to my employer, Samuel Oppenheimer of
Heidelberg."

"Oppenheimer, *potz tausend*," roared the Margrave
and slapped his thigh. "My Jew Oppenheimer. Why,
I'm on my way to him myself. Just look at 'em." He
pointed his riding crop at the soldiers who had retreated
under the branches of the tree. "This is supposed to be
my army—a sorry bunch of beggars."

Then he turned in the saddle. "Let's be on our way,
gentlemen. You, Emanuel, make room for this fellow
on one of the packhorses." He wiped the sweat from his
red cheeks. "An' you, men, behave yourselves, or there'll
be floggings at camp. You'll be paid in a few days."

The cavalcade moved on, leaving the soldiers to look
sullenly after them.

A friendly young man who carried no weapons had
helped Samson onto a gentle horse which he kept holding
by the reins. With one hand the future financier still
clutched his bundle while the other held tightly to the
animal's mane. He had never sat on a horse before. It
was almost more frightening than the dagger at his
throat.

A few moments ago, Samson had dreamed of power
and wealth. Now he made a most ridiculous sight and
he knew it. But the young man at his side who continued to guide Samson's as well as his own horse smiled
encouragingly and said, "Just hold on, Samson. In an
hour, at the latest, we'll be at my father's house."

Emanuel Oppenheimer, the Court Factor's oldest son,
took Samson straight to his own room in the back of

the steep-gabled townhouse in Heidelberg. A surprised servant maid brought buckets of water. Samson scrubbed for a long time. Finally, dressed in a doublet and hose from Emanuel's wardrobe, he was led into the big counting room. Several clerks stood before high desks, and their quills flew diligently over large ledger sheets.

Samson wanted to stop and observe everything, but Emanuel walked on, and he had no choice but to follow him into another more comfortably furnished room.

The Margrave, still in his riding boots, stomped impatiently from one end of the room to the other. From time to time he took a pinch of snuff from a silver box as he passed the big table. The Court Factor sat in an oaken chair, his head buried in his hands as if in deep thought.

"I tell you, Samuel, I must have the money," the Margrave pleaded. "If I can't stop the French somewhere near the Rhine, they'll march straight to the Danube. The whole Empire will fall at Louis' feet like an overripe plum."

"How much?" The Court Factor did not look up.

"At least two hundred thousand thaler. I need fodder for the horses, grain for the men, gunpowder, boots, blankets, everything. And first of all, I need money to pay my soldiers. You must help me."

Finally Samuel dropped his arms. Samson noticed with surprise how tired he looked. His voice sounded bitter.

"How can I help you, Your Highness? You already owe me a huge sum. And so does the Emperor and the Elector of Saxony and the Archbishop of Mayence. And if I can't pay my subcontractors in Germany, in Amsterdam, in London, they go bankrupt and I do too."

"You bankrupt? One of the richest men in the Empire? I can't believe it. You always come out on top."

"I have so far, Sire, but how often was it only by sheer luck? If my credit's gone, I'm finished. Then Samuel Oppenheimer will be just another ghetto Jew, but more probably he'll rot in debtor's prison."

The two young men stood respectfully by the door waiting to be noticed. Samson listened with growing amazement. Here sat his future master, his model, heavily humped over the handsomely inlaid table. His face was drawn, his forehead creased in deep wrinkles. So there was another side to the life in palaces and the friendship of princes.

The Margrave tapped the financier's hunched shoulder. "Samuel, you're my only hope. I've been to the Christian merchants. Nobody'll give me credit. Too much of a risk, they say."

"But the Jew can take the risk, eh? What has he to lose? All my life I've been dancing on top of a volcano. So far I've made out all right. And tomorrow? It's good we don't know what tomorrow will bring. Here, I advance you fifty thousand to pay your soldiers, and I'll write to my friends so they can start gathering the material you need."

"Thanks, Samuel." The Margrave heaved a sigh of relief and scooped up a double dose of snuff. "I knew I could count on you. If you ever get into real trouble, let me know. I'll stand by you."

"I might take you up on that promise, Your Highness."

Was this more than just a conversational phrase? To Samson it sounded like a prophecy.

"Why does he take such risks?" he asked himself. "He has been successful. He is rich. Can't he let well enough alone? When I get to the place where he is now, I'll learn to say no."

There was no time to figure out how he would improve on Oppenheimer's methods. The business conference was over. Now there was laughter and handshaking all around. Emanuel presented the new clerk to his father. Immediately the Margrave launched into an hilarious account of how he had found Samson on the road in an unusual horizontal position.

"I hope he'll never forget that you saved his life today," said the elder Oppenheimer. Then he opened the door and stood back. "Your Highness, will you honor me by being my dinner guest? I know you cannot stay long while the French are camping so uncomfortably close. I too am pressed for time. I'm leaving for Mannheim to attend my nephew's wedding. This way please."

It was the most magnificent meal Samson had ever seen. Seated around the big oval table were the Margrave with two of his officers, Samuel, his wife, and their sons and daughters.

Servants brought course after course on huge platters of hammered silver. Old wine gleamed dark-red in goblets of cut crystal. There were rare spices in finely wrought boxes, and from dainty cups of Chinese porcelain they sipped that costly new drink—coffee.

Samson sat silently between Emanuel and his younger brother, Lazarus. He hardly touched the food or drink. "The wedding." There seemed to be no room for any other thought in his numb brain. "Frumet's wedding."

It was a year later. Samson stood at one of the tall desks. The sheet before him was covered with long rows of figures. His right hand played with the quill while his left scratched lightly over the spot by his ear that had once been covered by the earlock. He was dressed in a fine cambric shirt. The black boots were long, in the latest fashion, with the tops turned down.

He was now perfectly at home in the counting room, through which drifted the scent of tea and spices from the Orient.

"Samson, Father wants to see you."

Emanuel had quietly come up to his desk. His voice was soft and pleasant as always. They had become very good friends during the year. To Emanuel, Samson could talk about his ambitious dreams, and the master's son was a willing listener. He would not say anything; he just smiled. He was content to live in his father's shadow, always obedient, never questioning.

Now he led his friend to the warehouse where bale upon bale of the goods from the Indies lay, spreading fragrance through the whole house.

"I thought we were going to your father's study."

"Yes, in a moment. First I had to tell you the news. Father has arranged a marriage for me. It's Esther, the daughter of David Sinzheim."

"Sinzheim? That's one of his correspondents in Frankfort. And what do you say to it?"

"Say to it? What can I say? Guess I'll just marry her."

"Emanuel, be a man for once. Don't you have a will of your own?"

"What can I do?"

"Listen. We both know the business now pretty well. Let's go away together. I'm sure every general in Europe would be glad to have us in his service. Let's be on our own."

"No, Samson, I'm not like you. My place is with my father. He knows what's best for me."

Samson shrugged his shoulders.

"I guess you can't help being what you are just as I can't help being what I am. Now let's hear what your father wants."

Several clerks hovered around Samuel Oppenheimer taking dictation and searching through thick files. Others were coming and going carrying sheaves of paper. For a while the two friends stood watching. He barked orders like a commander directing a battle.

Finally he looked up. Noticing them, he pushed away a stack of papers and motioned his clerks to wait outside.

"Listen, you two. I have important news. Emperor Leopold has called me to Vienna. I must leave at once."

"Leopold?" Samson forgot that his employer did not like interruptions. "The one who drove out all Jews a few years ago?"

"Yes, the same. And he didn't have a change of heart

either." The grey eyes gleamed proudly under bushy brows. "He just can't get along without me. The Turks are marching on Austria. His treasury is empty. His court is graft-ridden. He promises me any privilege I want, and I'll hold him to it. He'll treat me as no ruler has ever treated a Jew before."

He leaned back. His breast seemed to swell visibly.

"I want both of you to take charge of things here while I'm away. I'll give you your instructions now, and you better stick to them."

He looked sharply at Samson whose glance remained cool and steady.

The three men remained closeted for a long time. Samuel Oppenheimer did the talking while his assistants took notes.

Suddenly the door was thrown open, and an excited clerk stormed in.

"Didn't I give orders that I don't want to be disturbed?" snarled the master.

"Excuse me, sir, but a message from the synagogue . . . you're wanted there."

"What's going on at the synagogue? This is a working day."

"Refugees from Mannheim have come in, a whole host of them. They need help desperately."

Samson stiffened at the mention of Mannheim. His lips trembled slightly.

"Mannheim? Yes, I've heard," remarked the Court Factor. "They have smallpox there."

"There was rioting," reported the clerk. "The old

rumors, you know—the Jews poisoning the wells. A mob broke into the ghetto, but our young men fought 'em back. The city fathers don't want any riots, but they're scared. They advised that all Jewish women and children be sent away for a while. About fifty just arrived here, hungry, scared to death, some of 'em sick."

"Hm, they always come to me. Aren't there any other Jews in Heidelberg?" The gruff words could not hide the satisfaction of the speaker. "I can't get away now. Must get ready for the trip, and there are still mountains of work waiting. You, Emanuel and Samson, go and see what can be done for those people. You may spend as much money as is necessary."

Samson did not want to go. But before he could think of an excuse, Emanuel, dutiful and obedient as ever, was already on his way. Reluctantly, Samson followed him.

It was a short walk along the bank of the Neckar. From the hill the ornate castle glistened, but there was no time now to admire its newly rebuilt white walls. By the inn with the sign of the elk's head they turned into a short narrow street. The synagogue was the last building.

People crowded around the entrance. Women, shapeless in their dark wraps, and children carrying blankets were being led away by hospitable Heidelberg Jews. Others still stood in the doorway and in the tiny courtyard, dazed and bewildered.

Samson pushed past them into the prayer hall which was almost deserted. A woman sat in the far corner bent over the baby in her arms. A hood hung deep into her young face. In the dim light she was no more than a dark shadow. But Samson knew her instantly.

As his steps creaked closer on the worn floor boards Frumet raised her eyes. For a moment she stared at him in disbelief. Then her head fell again, and under the folds of the cloak her body shook with convulsed sobs.

Gently, Samson placed his arm around her shoulder and began to lead her to the door.

"Hush now," he whispered. "It's only a short walk to Uncle Samuel's house. There you will rest, and the baby, too."

Outside, the refugees were crowding around Emanuel, everybody trying to talk at the same time. Slowly, carefully, Samson led the young matron down the street. He supported her like something very fragile.

"This must have been a terrible trip for you. I wish I had known of it earlier."

She was silent. He could feel the warmth of her body as she leaned against him for support like a frightened little child.

What else was there to say? Several times he cleared his throat. Then he asked haltingly, "And your husband? Is he all right?"

"Nathan is dead." Her voice was raw and toneless. "He died of the smallpox four days ago."

Chapter **4**

Tulln was usually a sleepy little town. Its white-washed farm houses were crowded around the twin steeples of a very old church with peeling masonry. Its only claim to importance was that it lay on a much traveled road to Vienna. At Tulln, the road crossed the Danube River on a trestled bridge.

But on that September day in 1683 town and bridge were anything but a peaceful sight. The bridge was tightly packed with men, horses, and wagons moving slowly, like an endless black worm. The overflow was backed up into the town, filling every inch of the crooked streets. Boats and barges of all descriptions shuttled back and forth almost blotting out the sight of the water.

This was a relief army on the march, an army made up of soldiers from many Christian countries. It was the last hope of Vienna, the Austrian capital, which was cringing under the heavy siege guns of the Turkish generalissimo Kara Mustapha.

Samson Wertheimer, in dusty travel clothes, tried to

push his way through the throng—a tiresome undertaking. Dragoons in shining breastplates leaned against the houses, holding their horses by the reins. On the cobblestones of a side alley sat a band of musketeers, their ammunition-filled bandoliers slung over their frock coats. Many had taken off their wide-brimmed sweaty hats. They were singing a sad Slavic tune.

Another street was filled with artillery pieces; clumsy short mortars and culverins, each with a team of sturdy drafthorses. The canoniers were loudly teasing the frightened peasants, who tried to drive cattle, swine, and flocks of geese towards the bridgehead.

Samson was exhausted when he finally arrived at the gaily painted front of the town hall. The two fierce-looking sentries at the entrance lowered their sabres when he showed them a letter with the imperial seal. In constant danger of being knocked down by rushing couriers, he climbed the broad stairway.

In the council room King John Sobieski, leader of the relief forces, had made his temporary headquarters. The Polish ruler, a powerfully built man with a drooping mustache, was talking with a group of officers. A huge map was spread out on a table. Couriers were reporting on Turkish vedettes that had been sighted in the neighborhood.

John Sobieski looked as if he had slept in his clothes for several days, or rather, he seemed not to have slept much at all lately.

Samson stood at the door and hesitated to interrupt the King. Finally, he stepped forward and cleared his throat.

An officer who had been studying the map looked up. "Well, well, if it isn't Oppenheimer's young helper. What brings you here? Hope you're not in trouble again. Want to join us an' chase the Turks? It won't be a picnic, I can assure you."

Samson was glad to recognize his protector, Margrave Louis of Baden. The old warrior looked happy, like a hunting dog on the fresh track of game.

"This is a pleasant surprise, Your Highness." Samson braced himself against the Margrave's powerful handshake. "I am asking permission to join the relief army. I must get to Vienna."

"So must we. Question is: will the Turks let us?"

The King did not pay any attention to the newcomer. The couriers kept coming and going in a steady stream.

Now he looked up from the map.

"Margrave Louis, where are you?"

"Here, Majesty. May I present a fine lad, fellow by the name of Wertheimer, an assistant to the Court Factor. I think he can do us a lot o' good, you know, getting us the things we can throw at Kara Mustapha."

Deep lines of fatigue showed in the King's face. He had not listened too closely. "Yes, yes, we can use him. Always short of supplies. Hard to get anything from those thieving peasants. Here, Prince Eugene, look after him. See how he can help us."

A new courier was already whispering in the King's ear about some delay on the bridge. The merchant was forgotten.

Samson fingered the feather in his cap. Should he sneak out quietly or wait for another chance to attract the king's

attention? Then he felt a slight tug on his sleeve, and
somebody led him out of the room into the courtyard.

"I am Prince Eugene of Savoy," said the young man
at his side. "And your name is Wertheimer. I just heard.
How did you happen to get here just when we are crossing the river for the last lap of our journey?"

Although the Prince spoke a heavily accented German,
his language was cultured and refined. Samson felt immediately drawn to this slightly built youth with the un-
usually high forehead and bushy black eyebrows. There
was charm in his manner, an elegance that reminded
him more of the salon than of the battlefield.

Feeling surprisingly at ease, Samson launched into
the full story of his errand. Emperor Leopold had thrust
the handling of practically all the imperial finances on
Samuel Oppenheimer and, in addition, commissioned
him with provisioning his armies on several battle-
fronts. It was a giant task filled with difficulties and
dangers. About a year ago, he had called his son Emanuel
to Vienna to assist him, and now Samson, too, had
orders to move from Heidelberg to the Hapsburg capital.

Because he was urgently needed, Samson felt duty-
bound to reach Vienna as soon as possible. Of course,
when he left Heidelberg he had no way of knowing that
Vienna was cut off from the outside world.

"You won't let your master down, I see," said the
Prince. "Not every employee will venture through a
hostile army to reach his post."

"You see, Highness, our whole profession is built on
mutual trust. Oppenheimer gave me a chance to make

something of myself. Now when he needs me by his side, I want to make every effort to get there."

"You can make the effort. The success will depend on our guns and sabers. I hope you realize that we are greatly outnumbered. I command a regiment of Badish mounted grenadiers. We will cross in about two hours. It will be my pleasure to have you join me."

"I haven't told you yet—my wife and children are traveling with me. I left them at the house of Isaac Landauer, the Jewish merchant. I suppose they'll have to stay there for the time being."

"I should say so. You are lucky you brought them this far without being molested by marauders. Here, take this horse. I will accompany you to Landauer's house. You will have barely enough time to say good-bye."

The two riders found the street even more crowded than before. Soldiers tried to clear a path when they recognized the young officer. Even so, they moved at a snail's pace.

The Prince kept up a friendly chatter. Samson felt as if he had known him for a long time.

"Allow me a question," Samson finally asked. "I have been wondering about your accent. In the Rhineland where I come from, we hear it often. Are you by any chance a Frenchman?"

"Correct guess," laughed the Prince who was about six years younger than Samson. "And now you wonder what a Frenchman is doing in a campaign, bringing relief to the enemy of Louis XIV?"

With frankness, Eugene told him how his family had

destined him for the church. As a child he was called
"the little Abbé." But despite his slight stature he had
been determined to be a soldier. With the thoroughness
of a scholar he had pored endlessly over books on
weapons and strategy. Then he had asked the King for
a post in the army. Louis had sent him away scornfully.
Now, more determined than ever to make war his business, Eugene was on his way to offer Emperor Leopold
his sword and his loyalty.

"You are already fighting for the Emperor," said Samson. "As an officer of the relief army you are assured a
cordial reception."

"Hm, no need to relieve His Imperial Majesty. Don't
you know that he fled Vienna just before the Turks cut
the last road?"

"I didn't know. I would have thought that a ruler
belongs with his people in time of need. But then, I
don't understand anything about high politics."

"You'll learn fast, Samson, and it won't all be nice and
pleasant. Well, here is Landauer's house. I'll wait for you.
Don't tarry too long. My grenadiers are getting impatient."

Samson rushed inside. Frumet sat near the window.
Wolf, their baby boy, slept soundly in her arms while
Samson's four-year-old stepson, Isaac, sat on the floor
playing with a tiny kitten.

Samson kissed his wife with infinite tenderness.

"What did you find out?" she asked. "Can we travel
to Vienna?"

"I will go with the troops. You and the children must

stay here. With the help of God I will send for you in a few days."

"So the Turks are besieging the city. And you want to fight your way in with the relief army. Sam, let's go back. You're not a fighting man."

Samson thought she was more beautiful than ever: dainty as a porcelain figurine. But her eyes were sad and misty.

"I will miss you, my love. I'll miss you very much. But Uncle Samuel needs me. I can't let him down. I'm sure we will win this campaign."

"We?" A frown formed on her alabaster forehead. "Why are *you* concerned with all this? Christian fighting Moslem—what is it to us Jews?"

"Jews must be loyal when they pledge loyalty. I want to show them that Jews can fight if necessary."

"O Sam. You, a scholar, how can you talk like this? Jews don't kill. They pray for the Messiah, the bringer of peace."

The spell of Judah Chassid was hard to break. Samson moved back a step, and his face was clouded. He scratched his left ear.

"When is he coming? Next year or in a thousand years? In the meantime we have to live. And I mean to make sure that you and the children live well."

"Can't you think of anything but wealth? Gold brings sorrow and evil."

"Frumet dear, you know I love you above everything. But you're like a child in such matters. I must look out for you even against your will. Now I have to go. Keep

Isaac indoors during the next days. You'll hear from me
soon. God bless you."

His lips brushed her wet cheek. His hand quickly
stroked her rich black tresses. Then he was gone.

From the crown of Bald Mountain the King looked
down upon Vienna.

The slender spire of St. Stephen's Cathedral dwarfed
the red slate roofs of the city. Bastions and earthworks
formed a protective half-circle, anchored on both ends to
the muddy Danube Canal. The Hapsburg capital looked
tiny and forlorn, like a deer backed against a cliff, surrounded by vicious hounds.

On the plain and up toward the slopes of the Vienna
Woods camped the Turkish army, at least 200,000 strong.
Above the endless lines of white and brown tents the
green standards of the Prophet fluttered.

Black smoke belched from row upon row of fat Turkish culverins and bombards. Sometimes there was a weak
answer from the city walls. But the contest was plainly
uneven. The bastions showed ugly gaps which had been
hastily filled with rubble and boards. With eyes shaded
from the sun, one could see the blackened shells of
destroyed houses inside the ramparts.

"Looks bad," grumbled the King. "Count Starhemberg can't hold out much longer. It's a miracle he's still
keeping the Turks at bay with his 20,000. Probably no
more than half of them left by now. Poor starving fellows."

His commanders stood around him, watching the

silver-gray band of the Danube which, skirting the city to the north, lost itself in the mist rising from the Hungarian plains.

"We've only about 80,000 ourselves," reported a German general. "Half foot and half horse. The Grand Vizier can send half his army against us and still have enough to smash the city."

"I'm surprised he hasn't already attacked us. He's so sure of victory that he just ignores us."

"That may be his fatal mistake." It was Prince Eugene, by far the youngest of the commanders. "Kara Mustapha thinks the whole countryside is solidly in Turkish hands and that we're just an isolated band which he'll take care of in due time."

"That's probably it," growled Margrave Louis. His whiskers had taken on a lot of gray lately. "And what can we do up here? All we have is a good view."

Eugene stepped closer to the King. Even with his three-cornered hat, he reached only to the royal mustache.

"We must mount a general attack immediately and have the Viennese launch a sortie at the same time, throwing in their last strength. A quick breakthrough before Kara Mustapha can rally his far-flung forces—it's our only chance."

"Sounds good," pondered John Sobieski. "But it would take perfect coordination. We must send a messenger to Count Starhemberg."

"Through the whole Turkish army?" The Margrave was extremely doubtful. "That would take a fellow with the courage of a lion and the brain of a philosopher."

"I may have just the man for you," said the Prince.
"I'll be back shortly."

He returned after a while, followed by Samson Wertheimer.

"The Jew?" Sobieski sounded more than doubtful.
"You think you could do it?"

"Honor me with your trust, Your Majesty," said Samson. "From here I can see the enormous Turkish baggage
train. It is parked at the edge of the village of Nussdorf
at the foot of this hill. There must be sutlers and
peddlers of various tongues. When I studied in Poland
I picked up enough Slavic words to get by. If I can sneak
into this confusion of wagons, livestock and people,
nobody'll suspect me. Then I'll see that I get close to
the walls and have myself taken prisoner. What do you
want me to tell the count?"

"Brave lad," said the King. "Many of my nobles could
use some of your courage. Tell Starhemberg to be ready
day after tomorrow at sun-up. Three red rockets from the
top of this hill will be the signal. Then everybody who can
still crawl must get out and make all the noise possible.
Let them shoot off their last shot of grape. If you're
lucky, I'll see you in Vienna that evening. If not—well,
good-bye now."

Hours later a solitary figure could be seen pulling a
tightly-packed mule along the road to Nussdorf. Despite
the warm day, he wore a tattered fur cap. His coarse
blouse and baggy linen pants were frayed. On his dust-
streaked face he wore a stupid look.

As he plodded along he seemed to hear Frumet's voice, "Christians or Moslems? What is it to us Jews?" But this time, if he succeeded, she would be proud of him. If not, at least the Oppenheimers would take care of her and the little ones.

A patrol of Turkish cavalry in long cloaks rode up. Their round shields and peaked helmets shone red in the evening sun. They shouted something at the mule-driver and poked their curved swords into one of the sacks. A thin line of yellow wheat kernels trickled into the dust. The driver grinned foolishly and pointed in the direction of the village. They spat contemptuously and rode on.

Samson entered the village. Turkish officers were quartered in the houses. Without looking up, he trotted by them until he came to the marketplace, which was crammed with wagons. The heavy smoke from the cook-fires irritated his eyes, and his nostrils were assailed by the smell of burning fat. There was loud bickering in Turkish, Hungarian and several Slavic languages.

As night came the people bedded down in the wagons or huddled by the fires wrapped in coats and blankets. They sang and joked until the fires burned low. Then they fell silent, one after another.

John Sobieski's emissary sat with them. The first part of his task was done, but the really dangerous part would come tomorrow. He shivered in his thin blouse.

The metallic blare of long Turkish fanfares awakened him before dawn. Squadrons of horsemen were rushing through the streets. Without concern, they trampled the sleepers in the marketplace. Samson quickly rolled over on the cobblestones to escape a sharp hoof.

Slowly he rose, rubbed his eyes, and stretched his arms. Then he sauntered off after the galloping horses.

Once outside the village he broke into a steady trot. He took to the fields and vineyards that lined the road. Far ahead he could see a forest of lances with tufts of horsehair tied to the tips. The dreaded Janissari stood in silence waiting for the signal to attack. These shock-troops were held back till lesser units had sacrificed themselves and tired out the enemy.

Now Samson could see a gate open. A motley crew emerged from the city: soldiers clad in many different colors, and civilians wearing doublets and frockcoats. They charged across the cleared space that was marked from days of heavy shooting.

A bugle split the air, and the horse-hair lances were lowered. In precision rows the green-and-purple clad Janissari advanced shouting "Allah-al-illah."

This was the moment Samson had waited for. He crouched behind treestumps and heaps of masonry. Then he jumped forward, staying at a safe distance from the actual fighting. He remained unnoticed. Everyone had his hands full killing and staying alive.

Under the impact of the Janissari assault the sortie weakened. Many Viennese lay trampled and speared on the ground. The others rushed back through the gate. It swung shut as soon as the last of the besieged men had returned.

The Janissari halted just outside the range of musket-balls and grape that peppered them from the city walls. Finally they turned back and shouted words of scorn at the breathless defenders.

An Austrian officer took off his steel cap. His forehead was bleeding.

"We lost some good men again," he muttered, "An' we can ill spare 'em."

He looked around to take stock of his platoon. Suddenly he noticed a figure in dirty peasant clothes trying to hide behind a tall pikeman.

"Who's this?" he shouted. "Must've come in with us through the gate. A Turkish spy."

Several hands reached out for Samson. A brutal kick sent him sprawling to the ground.

"Get a rope," shouted the officer. "We can't make much fuss about heathen spies. Won't waste our precious food on 'em."

Soldiers rushed to bring a piece of hemp while Samson picked himself painfully off the ground.

"Listen to me, Captain," he pleaded. "For God's and your city's sake, listen."

"What's that?" The officer was shocked when he heard himself addressed in good German. "Ah, you're a clever spy. Doubly dangerous. Make haste with that rope."

A throng of spectators had formed. Hate glinted in their eyes.

"Give me a minute please. Take me to Count Starhemberg at once. Your lives depend on it. I have a message from King John Sobieski."

"Bah, perhaps from the Pope himself too? Poor devil.

Can't blame you for trying t' get your neck out of the noose. But it's no use."

"Here, look at this." Samson reached inside his blouse and ripped something off.

"*Donnerwetter*, where'd you get this? The King's seal on that golden ring. Are ye speaking the truth after all?"

"Now will you take me to Count Starhemberg?"

"By St. Stephen, I will. But if you've fooled us, you'll be sorry we didn't hang you right away. That much I can tell ye."

That night garrison and townspeople stayed up late. The last few landmines were readied. Ammunition was distributed until there was not a drop of lead to be had anywhere in the city.

Before sunrise Count Starhemberg and several of his aides stood in the tiny watchman's chamber high up on the steeple of St. Stephen's. The commander of Vienna was an old man. His gaunt body and red-rimmed eyes revealed the hardships of the past months. Samson stood behind him, flanked by two guardsmen with halberds.

There was a painful silence.

All eyes were turned toward the western hills. The one with the steep cliff descending straight to the Danube was Bald Mountain.

Now Count Starhemberg turned around. The bloody rim of the rising sun was already visible in the eastern sky.

"It's getting late. If this was a trick, Jew, you better confess now. Your end will be easier."

"I have nothing to confess, sir. You will soon see the signal, unless King John has been forced to change his plans."

"Change his plans, ha. You talked yourself out of the noose once. You'll not do it a second time."

A shout went up. Above the crowns of pine and fir on Bald Mountain rose a single red streak that burst into a cascade of fire. Then a second and a third.

"The signal," shouted the Count. "Ring the bells!"

The spire shook like a young tree in a storm as the big bell of St. Stephen gave out its first boom. Other churchbells chimed in, and their chorus drifted over the awakening city.

The Grand Vizier sitting high on his white charger was about to have the clarion blown for the daily assault. But before he could lift his hand, the city gates burst open. Practically the whole population came running across the flattened suburbs.

At the same time he heard screams behind him. He turned his impatiently dancing mount around.

The woods had come to life. Cannon fire flashed between treetops. The forest was disgorging streams of mounted men.

The Grand Vizier stroked his black beard nervously. He dispatched couriers to draw his far-flung lines together.

The relief army marched on, shouting with the lust to fight. German pikemen, eight ranks deep, strode in the center. With their long weapons resting on each other's shoulders, they looked like a giant, square porcupine.

On the flanks were Swiss musketeers and Bohemian grenadiers.

The grenadiers halted and hurled their clumsy explosives at the Turks. Not many hit their targets, but they made plenty of noise. Dust mingled with sharp metal fragments. Nervous Arabian horses shied.

Now the pikemen quickened their pace while the muskets at their side began to chatter. At the same time the Polish cavalry emerged from the woods. They fanned out and swept in wide arcs around the flanks of the waiting Janissari. John Sobieski himself led the charge on the left flank. On the opposite side rode Prince Eugene, far ahead of his regiment.

The besiegers had suddenly become the besieged. The attack was gaining ground. Landmines exploded with a deafening roar. The crowns of the ramparts were a solid black mass of men and women firing away with every weapon at hand, while below them Count Starhemberg's regulars pushed ahead.

Kara Mustapha's eyes swept around in a full circle. The two columns of enemy cavalry were closing in fast, and it would take hours until the giant half-moon of his siege army could be concentrated on this danger spot.

With a hefty curse he gave his stallion the spurs. The animal's forelegs rose high into the air, and then it shot away towards the bank of the Danube where the enormous fleet of Turkish barges was tied up.

Terror swept the Sultan's army as they saw their leader rush off in flight. The green standards were gone. Horsemen and foot soldiers were fleeing in a wild stampede, trampling each other mercilessly to death. Tents, pack animals, stores: the whole Turkish train, including Kara Mustapha's palace-like tent, remained behind.

Samson was still in the tower, but he was alone. Even his guards were gone.

Now he could see, far below, Count Starhemberg's men stream back to the city linking arms with King Sobieski's pikemen and musketeers. Women and children came running to greet the liberators.

Slowly he descended the narrow winding staircase. The big plaza in front of the cathedral was filling up. The church bells kept up an incessant clanging.

Several priests had rushed out of the sanctuary to open the huge bronze doors so that people could assemble to give thanks.

"Tell me," Samson asked one of them. "Where can I find Samuel Oppenheimer, the Court Factor?"

"Oppenheimer, the Court Jew?" The elderly clergyman was surprised. "You must be a stranger. Don't you know what happened to him? I wouldn't advise you to seek him out. But if you must, you'll find him in the city prison. He was arrested two weeks ago on special orders of the Emperor."

Chapter **5**

On his rented brown gelding Samson rode along the *Glacis*, the broad strip of green outside the bastions of Vienna. The bodies of men and horses had been removed, but the grass was still littered with the debris of the recent battle.

Samson had practiced horsemanship during the last years and it had brought him into contact with the nobility. Now he cut a handsome figure on his elegantly cantering mount.

The *Glacis* was filled with Viennese in their Sunday best. Carriages were parked along the bastion. Thousands stood around in groups discussing the dramatic events that were to be crowned by today's festivities.

Slowly, Samson passed a group of substantial burghers resplendent in high silk hats and holding gold- and ivory-tipped canes.

"So you've come out, too, to watch the Emperor's return, Master Pfitzer." The well-padded Viennese grinned and twirled his cane.

"Might as well enjoy the spectacle," answered his acquaintance. "Now since the danger's over, our dear Emperor is coming back again to look after his people. Isn't he precious?"

"Psst, not so loud." The padded one looked anxiously at a passing rider. "You never know who's listening." And bending to the other's ear, he whispered, "But you're right. Sobieski's done all the fighting, an' now when the air is clear our Poldi comes home to reap the glory."

Samson smiled as he rode on. He was trying to visualize how Leopold I, by God's Grace Ruler of the Holy Roman Empire and Sovereign of Austria and Hungary, would greet the Polish hero who was waiting for him on the cathedral steps.

He approached another group.

"I hear the Jew Oppenheimer's still in prison. May he rot there." It was a woman talking to her husband, obviously an artisan of some kind.

"Yes, that's where he belongs. It's because of him that prices are so high an' taxes keep mounting. Maybe now we'll have a little relief."

Samson spurred his horse angrily to get away from this poisonous talk. So Oppenheimer was being blamed for all the bad times and for all the extravagances of court and nobility. But how could one get the truth into the thick skulls of those fools?

Boom! Boom! The gelding shied. The rider's full attention was needed to keep the frightened animal from knocking down women and children.

Boom! Boom! On and on it went. The battery of

culverins at the west gate was not firing at a new enemy. It was a royal hundred-and-one gun salute.

A thick cloud of dust heralded the approaching procession. In the van rode a squadron of mounted grenadiers followed by the royal guards in close formation. On their black mounts the men, picked for their height, appeared even taller in their flowing white cloaks and with the high white plumes on their brightly polished helmets.

As the gilded imperial coach, drawn by eight snow-white mares, lumbered into sight, the church bells began to toll. A few hesitant shouts of welcome went up, but most citizens just stood with bared heads and kept a cool, respectful silence.

His tri-cornered hat in hand, Samson waited for the cortège to pass. As the last of the countless baggage wagons entered the city gate, he turned west, and in a lively trot followed the road on which the Emperor had been returning to his capital.

After more than an hour's riding, he noticed another much smaller dustcloud in the distance.

"This could be them," he shouted, and gave the gelding the spurs. It took off.

The rider drew reins sharply. Like a whirlwind he was off the horse. He tore open the door of the muddy travel coach and in the next instant he was hugging and kissing the woman and the children inside.

"Now stop that, Samson. You're hurting me, and the coachman can see us."

In mock protest Frumet tried to push him away, but

the radiant smile on her little pale face betrayed her real feelings.

"It's been so long." Unmindful of her words, he kissed her again and pressed the heads of the children against his body.

"Thank God you're strong and well," whispered Frumet. "I heard what you did. You are a hero now. But I should be angry. You never thought of us for a moment."

"I thought of you all the time."

"Dad, I want a Turkish sword." Isaac fingered the lace collar of his stepfather's shirt while little Wolf made happy gurgling noises.

"I have one at home. Let's get on now, and I'll show it to you. Frumet, you must be completely exhausted. Move on, coachman."

Holding the gelding to a slow trot, he kept pace with the coach as they rode on towards the Danube city.

Samson and his family were quartered on the fifth floor of the palatial Oppenheimer house on *Bauernmarkt*, the broad street with the market stalls where farmers sold their produce in the mornings. It was one of the finest houses in the city, with wrought-iron landings on the wide staircase and marble figurines in the hall.

But now, like a choking pall of smoke, despair and fear hung over the damask-lined rooms. Silently, the servants hurried by. The Court Factor's four daughters kept to their rooms for days, even during mealtime. When they had to cross a hallway one could see their eyes, reddened and swollen from crying.

Their father had been in prison for more than a month now. Nobody was allowed to see him. All they knew was that his old adversary, Bishop Kollonitz, had accused him of bribing government officials.

Samson, too, stayed in his suite most of the time. The inactivity forced upon him by his employer's absence made him nervous.

"Dad, let's play cavalry again. I'm the dragoon an' you're the horse."

Dutifully Samson crawled over the thick Persian carpet while Isaac rode on his back and squealed with delight. Wolf toddled alongside, shrieking at the top of his little lungs.

There was a knock at the door. A bearded Jew entered. He was one of the many refugees from persecuted communities who had been taken into the house as unnecessary servants. Only Samuel Oppenheimer and his household had permission to reside in Vienna.

"Master Emanuel wants to see you immediately in the counting room. It's extremely important, he says."

Emanuel was pacing up and down the long room. The row of tall desks, now unmanned, looked like a platoon of evil ghosts.

"How he has aged,"thought Samson. Compassionately he looked at his friend's face, which was gray from worry and sleeplessness.

In an armchair sat a stout well-groomed man in the modish dress of a courtier.

"Baron, this is our associate Samson Wertheimer."

The Baron gave a cool, hardly noticeable nod.

"Samson, Baron von Steinach has come with a secret message from the Emperor. I am to take my father's clothes, the ones he wears for court audiences, and go with him. Will you join me? It would give me more confidence."

"Why do you ask? You know I would never deny you help. But I don't know yet of what help I can be there." With effort, the Baron heaved himself out of the chair. "Let's be off then. We must hurry."

The carriage with the imperial coat of arms carried them to a bleak, fortress-like building with two sentry boxes flanking the heavy iron gate. It was the city prison.

The Baron showed some papers to a sentry, and the three men were admitted through a narrow side door. A slouching, dirty-looking turnkey conducted them through endless dark corridors, heavy with the stench of vermin and decay. From time to time unearthly shrieks, like voices from the nether world, echoed through the dripping stone vaults.

Finally the turnkey halted in front of a little iron door. A giant key grated in the lock. It took some time to make the rusty bolt move. Then it yielded with an ugly squeak, and the door groaned open.

The man whom Samson remembered as the elegant self-assured Court Jew bore no resemblance to the wretch who squatted on a filthy straw pallet in the semi-darkness of the cell. An unkempt gray beard framed a grimy face with lusterless eyes. The shirt which once had been white hung loosely from stooped shoulders.

"Up with you," rasped the turnkey. "You're to go to the provost's quarters an' get cleaned up."

The arms of his oldest son and of his assistant had to support Samuel Oppenheimer on the way to the chambers of the prison commander.

Leopold of Hapsburg was sitting in council.

Despite the roaring log fire in the enormous tiled fireplace, the octagonal, low-ceilinged room was cold and damp, as were all the innumerable throne rooms and ceremonial halls in the imperial palace.

Like statues, the guards stood by the closed doors, their long halberds resting on the parquet floors. It was a gloomy October day and candles burned in the crystal chandeliers.

The Emperor looked like the churchman he originally had wanted to be: slender, pale, bookish, clean shaven with thick, fleshy lips. He sat on a dais, while his courtiers stood below in a deferential half-circle. There were councilors in long ermine-lined cloaks, prelates in purple robes and birettas, and a sprinkling of military men with jewel-hilted ceremonial swords and clanking silver spurs.

"What news do you bring from Hungary, my Prince?" The Emperor addressed himself to Prince Eugene, now the youngest general in the imperial army. The Frenchman was dwarfed by the burly nobles from the various German, Slavic, Italian, and Belgian parts of the empire.

"I wish I could bring better news, Your Majesty."

"What? Have the Turks beaten you? I gave orders to avoid open battle. Who defied me?"

"Nobody, Sire. There was no major battle, and we were pursuing the enemy all through Hungary. But now the pursuit has stopped. That gives Kara Mustapha time to

collect reinforcements. If nothing is being done, the
Grand Vizier will soon be marching up the Danube
again."

"And why don't my generals do anything? Why don't
they harrass the Turk? That's the least they could do."

The Emperor gestured angrily. On his over-sized
throne he looked like a child.

"It's money, Your Majesty. Soldiers are deserting. Our
officers look more ragged than beggars. You can't fight
a tough enemy without weapons, without food, without
horses."

The other military men nodded in agreement while the
councilors wagged their wigged heads with concern.

"Money, money. That's all I hear. I had to pawn my
crown jewels to pay Sobieski's men, and then he wasn't
satisfied. Isn't there anybody in my lands who can handle
finances?"

He looked around. The councilors seemed to shrink
back from his gaze. Only Prince Eugene looked the
sovereign straight in the eye, and so did Margrave Louis
of Baden who stood by his side. The Margrave was now
the foremost general of the Emperor's armies.

"Kollonitz," shouted Leopold.

"At Your Majesty's service." The tall figure clad in
bishop's robes bowed slightly.

"You're the one who talked me into arresting Oppenheimer. Now you see in what a miserable state we are."

"I am most distressed, Majesty. All I wanted was to
have Austria served by honest Christians."

"Where are your honest Christians now? Where is their credit?"

The prelate kept his dignified composure. He spoke slowly:

"I had counted on the Bishop of Wuerzburg. He has important connections in the commercial world. But his friends can only deliver on a cash basis."

"Cash, bah, and fat profits too! I've had enough of your bishop and his friends. Why is it that only the Jew can handle these matters well when the need is greatest? Fortunately I have already taken steps." A sly smile played on his protruding lip. "Chamberlain, go see if they're here."

With a ceremonial bow, the chamberlain, in his gold-embroidered clothes, left the room. Heads were put together, and an unceremonious buzz rose from among the courtiers.

The chamberlain returned, followed by three men. "The Imperial Court Factor Samuel Oppenheimer and two associates," he intoned, tapping his eagle-topped staff on the floor. The three bowed low.

The Emperor seemed to be truly glad to see his factor. "Well, here's my Jew again. It's been quite some time. Have you decided to mend your ways?"

"Your Majesty, I don't need to mend my ways. I have always served you faithfully and will continue to do so."

The Court Factor looked haggard and sick. His speech was humble, yet dignified.

"You know quite well, Sire," broke in the Margrave of Baden, "that those were only trumped-up charges. He never did anything wrong except, perhaps, take too many risks in your behalf."

The old warrior sounded as gruff and forthright as always. Bishop Kollonitz bit his lip. His face was crimson, but he remained silent.

"Permit me, Your Majesty," said Oppenheimer calmly, as if wiping away the indignities of the last weeks, "to introduce my son Emanuel and my assistant Samson Wertheimer."

"Samson, I didn't recognize you in those fancy clothes. You look quite different from that bedraggled muleteer on the road to Nussdorf."

Impulsively, Prince Eugene stepped out of his place and pumped his friend's hand. Then he remembered the court etiquette that was so dear to his ruler. He turned to face the throne.

"Forgive my poor manners, Sire. But I had to greet a fine hero, one who had an important hand in our victory at the gates of this city."

In brief but enthusiastic words, he told of Samson's part in the breaking of the siege. The Emperor laughed heartily.

"So you fooled Mustapha's men. Brave lad. Too bad you're a Jew. I would've loved to give you a command in my armies."

Bishop Kollonitz scowled. He was the man who prided himself with having been responsible for the expulsion of the Jews from Vienna a few years earlier.

The young general linked arms with the young merchant. The powerful churchman shot glances of undisguised hatred at both of them. His ire had found new targets.

Samson's cheeks were flushed with pleasure. But the Bishop's stare did not escape him, nor did the frown that now marked Samuel Oppenheimer's forehead. Samson suddenly realized that the Court Factor was envious of all the praise he was getting.

"You make enemies quickly when you rise," he thought. But he stood back silently as the councilors began their deliberations on the complex financial needs of the empire.

There was a cheerful reunion at the house on *Bauern-markt*. The many grooms, clerks, maids and handymen, who had had little or nothing to do a short while ago, now went around with straight backs and confident smiles. The dark cloud had passed.

But the Court Factor himself was impatient. Hastily, he slipped away from the embraces of his wife and daughters, promising to spend more time with them later. To the many well-wishers of his household, he said, "Leave now, good people. I have some very urgent business to attend to."

Then he closeted himself with his sons Emanuel, Wolf, Abraham and Nathan, and with Samson and several trusted clerks.

The captain was again at the helm. One could almost see the color return to his cheeks and his stature grow by inches as he mapped out his plans to save the Empire from bankruptcy. The armies had to be kept in the field, armies fighting the Turks and the French, as well as several German and Italian princes. The Court Factor was again at his job of keeping the whole ponderous machine of power politics well-oiled with money.

"Get letters ready to be sent out by special couriers," he ordered his clerks. "Ask Itzig Koppel in Pressburg to procure 10,000 sacks of flour. Lazar Hirschl in Breslau should get us about three hundred oxen. Then write to Jacob Seliger in Venice for a thousand jugs of good wine for the officers. Then—let me see. Requests must go out to our correspondents in Poland for oats and rye and to Kiev for gunpowder. What else do we need? Horses, sand in sacks for the earthworks, boots for the cavalry, and for all men clothes and blankets. And send word to the merchants along the Danube to buy up all the barges and boats they can find."

Samson was writing. His master worked with furious speed. All his clerks were sweating to keep up with the rapid fire of orders. But they felt good, like horses under the control of competent riders. The master was back, and things were moving again.

Samuel Oppenheimer paused and hastily gulped a cup of wine which a footman offered him.

"That'll take care of the immediate needs." His eyes rapidly scanned a long list of his own notes. "I don't think I've forgotten anything important. Now comes the really tough task—asking those men to deliver on credit. Many haven't been paid yet for their last deliveries. That'll take some persuading."

He looked at his oldest son. Emanuel was happy that

his role as the temporary head of the Oppenheimer house had ended. "Emanuel, you had better see that our bags are packed. You and I will leave tomorrow after morning prayers. We'll go first to the Leipzig Fair, where we'll probably meet most of our sub-contractors. You, Samson—"

Samson's mind had wandered. He saw himself riding on a fiery charger at the side of Prince Eugene. Guiltily, his head jerked up, and his left hand reached for the spot by his ear.

"Yes, Reb Samuel?"

"You will stay here and be in charge of our Vienna office. And mark you. I want you to stick to the counting room. You're to wait for my orders before you run to court or to some mighty personage. Is that understood?"

"Yes, Reb Samuel."

Samson kept his composure, but underneath the calm a storm raged. So he should wither in the counting room while the master dealt with the men of means and influence. No such contacts for him.

Did the Court Factor already fear that he was grooming a competitor?

"I won't be locked away for ever," he thought grimly. "Am I some dangerous weapon that he is afraid to handle? He's scared it might go off in his face. Well, I'll do the chores around here, but my time will come, and I'll be ready."

He nearly crushed the quill in his fist as he bent over his papers again.

Chapter **6**

Samson Wertheimer had given one of his famous banquets. Now the guests were leaving. In the street, curious onlookers watched the noble ladies and gentlemen enter their carriages and drive off.

The Wertheimer house on Kaerntner Street was still new. It had been built after the Turkish siege. The street entrance was flanked by columns and plaster curlicues. A sentry in the uniform of the imperial guard paced up and down in front.

Samson stood in the huge diningroom. The snow-white damask tablecloth was now littered with the remains of a sumptuous meal. Candles were burning in burnished brackets along the wine-red wainscoting.

He stepped to a window and looked out on the finely trimmed arbors of his French garden. He could afford to give elegant parties now. As Oppenheimer's chief Viennese representative he was receiving 24,000 thaler a year plus commission. He was wealthy, and his influence reached into the highest circles.

And yet he was not in a pleasant mood.

Two guests had remained behind with him and Frumet; neither guest belonged to the aristocracy. One was Gotthold Regner, his old travel companion whom he had once helped escape from a duke's wrath. The other was a white-bearded Jewish patriarch.

Samson had looked forward to Gotthold's visit. They had written each other from time to time. Their letters were long, learned exchanges of ideas. Samson had found out that Gotthold was supporting himself very poorly as a tutor. He had invited him to Vienna, but the visit was turning out very disappointingly.

Samson turned from the window.

"Is this your final answer, Gotthold? I'm trying to get you a position in the imperial chancery, and you refuse?"

"I must, my friend. Don't you see?"

"No, I don't see. You're without employment, without funds. And here you refuse a position that'll give you a regular income. Besides, it has a great future for a man with your ability."

The tall philosopher put his long arm on Samson's shoulder.

"But can't you understand? I am a fighter. I fight not with a sword, but with ideas. And I must tell what I consider the truth. I cannot help a cruel, intolerant ruler keep his people down. I must be free."

"I understand you," said Frumet. "There are things more important than luxury."

She sat at the lower end of the long table. Her dark-blue frock was of an exquisite material, yet very simple.

Samson turned away. Harsh words formed on his lips, but he suppressed them.

"I guess a man has the freedom to starve if he so chooses. Perhaps you'll change your mind. Remember, I'm still your friend. You can always turn to me for help."

"You are a wonderful man, and I will always be grateful to you. I've a feeling that you're the one who will change his mind some day. Then you'll again be interested in other books besides ledgers."

A hopeful smile played on Frumet's lips as she watched the two men. Gotthold's eyes came to rest on her. He remembered:

"Samson, will you permit me to read your wife my most recent pamphlet on religious freedom? She expressed great interest."

Frumet glanced at the old rabbi who sat motionless in a corner. "Yes, come into the garden. It's such a lovely day. You can read to me in the rose arbor."

Samson remained alone with the shriveled old man. He paced the room several times before he addressed him. His smile looked artificial.

"Now, Reb Simon. It's good to see somebody from Worms. What's the news in my hometown? Have you come with a message?"

"Yes, Reb Samson." From the folds of his black cloak he produced a piece of parchment. "I bring a letter from your father."

Samson had not heard from his father for a long time. Reluctantly he began to read. The Hebrew letters

danced crazily before his eyes. Rabbi Wertheimer's hands
were shaky. He was writing from a sickbed which he
did not ever expect to leave. He regretted now that
he had once sent his son away with harsh words. But
with pride he had followed from a distance his rise to
fame and wealth. He was especially proud that God had
made his son an instrument for helping fellow-Jews in
distress. He was sending him his blessing, probably for
the last time.

The letter ended with a prayer that some day God
might lead his son back to the sacred studies for which
he had been trained.

Samson crumpled the paper and threw it on the table.
There it lay amid cake crumbs and half-filled glasses. He
resumed his pacing.

"Will you go to see your father before he dies?" asked
the old man in a toneless voice.

Abruptly Samson turned around.

"Why don't you leave me alone? All of you. I can't
help him. And here, matters that can shake the Empire
are at stake. I'm needed here. It's urgent."

"Only one effort is urgent—to learn and interpret the
word of God." The old rabbi spoke more to himself than
to anybody in particular. Then he raised his wrinkled face
and looked the financier straight in the eyes. "I'm returning to Worms. What shall I tell Rabbi Isaac?"

Samson opened his mouth and closed it again. What
was the use? Those people would never understand what
he was after. They knew nothing but their dank ghettoes
and stifling study rooms.

The old man sat motionless.

To his relief, Samson now heard a shuffling of feet at the door. His bookkeeper Hirschel Meier entered. He leaned heavily on his cane, dragging a lame foot behind him. Hirschel had come into Samson's employment with high recommendations. Even Bishop Kollonitz had dropped a word of praise for him. Yet Samson felt uneasy in his presence.

The bookkeeper sidled up to him. "Are you ready? We should be on our way to the hunting lodge. The Prince is coming, you know."

He grinned as if to show that he and the master shared important confidences.

Samson fidgeted. He cast sidelong glances at the old rabbi, who sat like a statue. "I must go now," he finally blurted out. "State affairs that cannot wait. Tell my father I will pray for his recovery. And as soon as I can, I will travel to Worms."

He rushed from the room followed by the hastily shuffling bookkeeper. In his heart he knew that he would never see his father again.

The summer morning was bright. The dew had disappeared from the meadows. Only an hour's ride from the city, the hunting lodge stood in a little clearing surrounded by forest thickets. Green shutters had been thrown open to let sunshine into the small backroom. From far off came the metallic calls of horns and the muted confusion of shouts.

Clad in brown kneebreeches and an open shirt, Samson

sat at a simple wooden table bent over stacks of paper, while Hirschel Meier stood by him. A simple breakfast of dark bread, butter and a flask of wine stood on the table. The food had been only slightly touched.

"Perhaps you should've gone along on the boar hunt, Reb Samson. After all, you invited them."

The bookkeeper was all deference.

"Fiddlesticks. They don't need me. That's sport for cavaliers. They enjoy sticking spears through those poor dumb beasts, and I don't."

"What's the use then owning such a fine hunting estate?"

"It's good for the business. That's what it is. If the woods're full of game, they don't even mind the Jew who invites 'em. Besides, I'm busy this morning. The Oppenheimers are returning, and I have to straighten out my accounts."

"You just work an' work, an' the Oppenheimers get all the glory. It's about time—"

"Enough of that, Hirschel. I don't want to hear any more. Let's get on with the figures."

"Listen, master. I think they're coming back."

The glade around the lodge began to fill with men. There came the beaters and the trumpeters and the dog handlers with their yapping charges straining at the iron chains. Clad in green with feathered caps, the noble guests followed on horseback. Behind them four sweating peasants carried a long pole from which hung the dark-gray carcass of a huge boar, its two vicious tusks scraping the ground.

Shouting and jostling, the crowd settled down on rough benches and on the grass while hefty maids brought out lunch on large wooden platters and in flagons.

The special guests, a dozen aristocrats and prelates, left their horses in the care of grooms and stepped into the main room of the lodge. Gloomily mounted elk- and boarheads looked down on them from the walls.

The guests sank heavily into leather chairs. While they waited for the feast, they made loud, passionate comments on this morning's chase. It had been a wise old animal, stubborn and dangerous. One of the horses had received a bloody rip in its flank before the crafty fellow was finally brought down by Prince Eugene's spear. No pistol was needed to finish off the grunting adversary.

Samson and his assistant remained in the backroom.

"Go, tell the Prince I'm waiting for him. And see that the guests have enough to eat and drink."

"And if they ask for you?"

"I'll join them after a while. The wine is strong. They won't miss me after the third cup."

"Yes, sir."

Hirschel Meier shuffled out and returned shortly with the Prince, whose riding garb was dusty and torn in places. He looked tired, but his eyes still sparkled with the excitement of the last hour.

The bookkeeper hovered in the background.

"Hirschel, I told you to look after the guests."

Reluctantly Meier closed the door behind him.

"I don't trust that assistant of mine too much, my Prince."

"Can't blame you. There's a shifty look in his eyes."

"I'm uneasy in his presence. Nothing definite that I know. But I've a feeling he's spying on me, perhaps for our mutual friend, the Bishop."

"So that's where the wind blows. Let's make sure he's not eavesdropping."

The Prince opened the door a slit and peered out. Then he closed it again and took possession of the only comfortable chair in the room. He cut his voice down to a whisper:

"This time the Bishop is really out to destroy me."

"Are you sure?"

"Not the slightest doubt. You know very well how he's been trying for years to block my way at every move."

"I know. But despite everything, you won one victory after another. And now you're the great hero. The wine lovers in the taverns and the urchins in the street are even singing a song about you:

> Prince Eugene, the noble knight,
> For the Emperor he won back
> City and fortress—"

"Stop it. You're better with figures than with tunes. Yes, I was fortunate. We've beaten the Turks in many a battle. They've run from us clear to the far end of Hungary. But now Kara Mustapha is massing a tremendous force at the Theiss River. If he's not stopped, we'll soon see the standards of the Prophet at the gates of Vienna again."

"Aren't you going to do anything about that, my

Prince? I thought you were about to leave for Hungary to join the army."

"I'm leaving in three days, but it's the old story." The Prince jumped up and stepped close to the table, gripping its edge with nervous hands. "No money, no ammunition, no horses. And I'm convinced that my armies are being starved intentionally."

"How so? You mean the Emperor doesn't *want* to win?"

"Oh he wants to win, but he's far from the scene. The Bishop has his ear and makes capital out of my French background. He warns him that I might make a deal with Louis, if I get too big. It's like running against a stone wall."

The knuckles on the table's edge were white.

"What will you do, my Prince?"

"I'm going to fight Kara Mustapha, if I have to do it with my bare hands. But it'll be an uneven fight."

"This could be the battle of all battles. If you win, it will be the end of Kara Mustapha and of the Turkish menace. Your place in history will be secure."

"If, if—" The slender general was now pacing the small room at a furious speed. "The history books never mention those who could've been successful, if others hadn't thrown sticks into their path."

Samson sat very quietly watching his friend. Finally, when he spoke, his words were barely audible:

"What you need is a good purveyor."

"I know. Oppenheimer's helped me much in the past, but he's in over his ears with the armies in Italy and the

Palatinate. Besides, I'm a very poor risk what with Kollinitz against me and the Emperor weak and easily swayed."

"Would you take me as your purveyor?"

Abruptly the Prince stopped his pacing.

"You, Sam? You must be drunk from your own wine. You're Oppenheimer's agent."

"I am now, but I need not always be. In fact, long ago I decided to cut loose and become independent. I would be greatly honored to have you as my first client. My skill, as well as my affection, are yours, my Prince."

Samson had risen. His eyes were very serious, yet a warm little smile played on his lips.

"Samson, I don't know what to say. Of course, I'd be overjoyed to have you in my service. But I'm thinking of you. Oppenheimer may be a stern master, but he will surely be a dangerous competitor. The stakes are high in this game, and the players are ruthless. And what can I offer you? The uncertainty of war. If I lose, I drag you down with me into ruin."

"I've thought of all that. Risk is a daily companion in my work. And further, there is more to be considered here than success."

"More? What more?"

"I want to serve not only the Prince, but the man Eugene. I want to support what he stands for—kindness, courage, love of the fine and noble things in life—"

Both men seemed embarrassed to reveal their feelings for each other. The frail aristocrat swallowed a few times before he said, "Well, Samson, if that's the way you feel, welcome on board the little pitching ship. We'll keep 'er afloat, or sink together."

His white hand looked dainty, but it managed a surprisingly strong, man-size handshake.

"Let's drink to our partnership," he proposed. The two men clanged the silver goblets together and then drained them to the last drop.

"Now, my Prince." Samson slipped back into his business-like manners. "I'll return to Vienna as soon as my duties as host permit it. Even before then I'll send off a letter to Samuel Oppenheimer, terminating our relationship. After that, all my time and strength will be devoted to your campaign. I'll join you at your headquarters as soon as my preparations in the capital are completed."

Side by side the two men, so unlike in stature and background, stepped through the door into the large front room. A strong smell of wine assailed their nostrils, and the sounds of men singing loudly and gaily off-key hammered against their ears.

Chapter 7

The Danube River meandered lazily through the yellow plains of Hungary. Wheat fields and pasture lands stretched endlessly beyond the river marshes. Here and there the monotony of the scene was broken by groups of low-slung houses. Their thatched roofs were dwarfed by the long poles which served as levers to raise buckets from water wells.

Slowly the flotilla of a dozen flat barges moved down the river. The tillermen kept the vessels close together. The pilot in the lead barge knew the river like his own back yard. They traveled only by night.

This part of Hungary was once again in Austrian hands, but the inhabitants could not be trusted. Many loathed the Hapsburg rule. The Hungarian nobles especially had enjoyed many privileges under the Turkish pashas.

Samson stood by the pilot. He wore a long sheepskin coat with the fur turned inside and a high fur cap. He was worried.

During the day, while the barges lay hidden behind

the willows of an island, he had noticed some activity on the bank. Peasants had been scurrying around. A horseman had appeared and then sped away eastward.

Turkish patrols might still be lurking around. Perhaps the barges had been discovered. If they were to fall into a trap, it would be the end of cargo as well as crew. One spark, one shot fired into the right spot could blow them all sky-high.

The flat boats were loaded with kegs of gunpowder. Lead cannister and grape shot were stacked up tightly and covered with canvas. Large wooden tubs contained the fuses of slow-burning powder, each wrapped in cloth to keep the moisture out. Iron balls of different sizes were arranged in low pyramids.

Samson fingered the last dispatch from the Prince. It had been delivered by a tight-lipped swineherd. "Hurry, hurry," it said. "Kara Mustapha is getting ready to slip across the Theiss River into the Transsylvanian Mountains. Unless he is stopped, he will recruit there the mightiest army Europe has ever seen. And then woe to us next spring. My artillery is virtually out of ammunition—"

Hurry, hurry. The great lords were always in a hurry and short of cash.

Samson peered into the silent fog. Why wasn't he in his beautiful house with his family? Frumet had not even wanted to say good-bye to him when he left. She loved him, of that he was sure. And yet they were drifting farther and farther apart. He knew she was still corresponding with that half-crazed Judah Chassid, the forerunner of the Messiah. Was he really a lunatic? Was there less sense in his visions than in a Court Jew's running after fame and wealth?

Yes, he had servants and carriages. The counts and even the princes of the blood delighted in the offerings of his table and cellar.

He thought of Samuel Oppenheimer, his former master, now his rival. One day he was the power behind the throne, the privy councilor of kings and cardinals. The next day he was headed towards the debtor's prison, the howl of a bloodthirsty mob ringing in his ear.

But the Prince was waiting on the Theiss River. The Prince trusted him with the sacred trust of a friend.

The pilot steered his barge towards a narrow channel between the north bank and a long island. "What a perfect spot for an ambush," thought Samson.

As if in answer to his thoughts, shots crackled ahead of them. Thin blue flames from gun muzzles flared up on the bank and the island. The channel was blocked by crossfire.

The crewmen were rushing around in confusion, knocking each other against the kegs and iron balls. They knew that once in the channel, they would be sitting ducks for the sharpshooters.

"Can you steer 'round the tip to the far side o' the island?" shouted Samson.

"We'll try," yelled the pilot. "It's shallow there, but we might get by."

The stub-nosed bow swung around, and the water lapped protestingly against it. Avoiding a large boulder

by a hair's breadth, the barge crept along the sandy tip
of the island. On other islands farther away waterfowl
were beginning to call loudly against the disturbance.

While the invisible enemy kept up its murderous
crossfire, the ammunition barges halted out of range.
There was hardly any current. A further advance might
beach the boats in the shallow water.

At Samson's order the men quickly removed grape-
shot and cannister from the last barge leaving, however,
a good-sized portion of gunpowder. Then the barge
turned once more into the channel, and the crewmen
swung themselves overboard. They quickly found refuge
on the other eleven vessels, while the abandoned barge
drifted slowly towards the point on which the fire from
island and bank converged.

The flotilla rested motionless on the river side of the
island. Samson waited. The wait seemed endless.

Suddenly there was a terrific roar. A huge white flash
lighted up the moonless sky. They could hear the
triumphant shouts of the invisible enemy.

"Now, men," hissed Samson, pistol in hand. From
the barges that had been tied together, men jumped overboard and splashed through the murky water. They
were armed with handguns, with knives and cutlasses,
with anything they had grabbed in the darkness. They
took the few Turks on the island by complete surprise.

It was not a fight, it was a slaughter. No quarter was
given. The Austrians combed the island systematically
and made sure they had not overlooked any enemies.

A veiled moon had come up and it lighted the ghastly

scene. Samson saw Saracen soldiers kneel and raise their arms wailing, *La ilaha illa Allah,* until their throats were slit by knives.

Then he heard another voice. It came from behind a tree. He charged around it with pistol cocked. Then he stopped and stood rigid. He saw a man with arms raised high. The man was proclaiming in a loud, but shaky voice, *"Sh'mah Yisrael*—Hear, o Israel, the Lord, our God, the Lord is One."

"What are you, a Turk or a Jew? Speak up quickly. You haven't much time."

"I am a Turkish Jew. My name is Z'vi ben Menasse, o gracious master. Please let me finish my prayers before you kill me."

"Come with me quickly," whispered Samson. "Bend low so they won't see you."

They reached the first barge while the extermination on the island continued. Z'vi was the only survivor.

Hastily Samson made his prisoner remove the tell-tale turban and the sash around his waist. He gave him a spare sheepskin coat and cap. By morning he would have to invent a likely explanation for the presence of an extra bargehand.

When the sun rose the first crows began circling over the island of death. Their ugly cries silenced the gentle murmur of the water.

The bank was still. The Turks who had fired from there had probably disappeared, thinking their mission accomplished.

Samson was anxious to continue the journey. They

were not far from the confluence of the Theiss and the
Danube. That evening he hoped to reach Prince Eugene's
camp.

As the eleven barges got under way, the survivor began
to tell Samson about his life. He was a Sephardic Jew, a
descendant of Spanish refugees. While Jews were not
ordinarily drafted into the Turkish armies, some spiteful
pasha who was incensed at Z'vi's father had sent him off
with a band of conscripts.

To his amazement, Samson learned that the Turks
generally treated Jews and followers of other non-Moslem
religions with kindness, apparently much better than did
the Christian rulers. There were great congregations,
proud synagogues and renowned schools of Hebrew
learning in the Ottoman empire.

More than ever Samson wondered why he was rushing barge-loads of death to a battle that was not his
battle.

Prince Eugene, Fieldmarshall of Austria and com-
mander-in-chief of all forces fighting the Ottoman Sultan,
stood on the crown of a hill overlooking a bend in the
Theiss River. His frail body was wrapped in a simple gray
cape. From his small pale face giant black eyes peered
intently into the swiftly deepening darkness of the early
evening.

Members of his staff stood back at a few respectful
paces. The encampment of soldiers was hidden in the
oak forest. They were eating cold rations this evening.
The making of a fire or any loud noises were strictly for-

bidden. The subdued murmur of 50,000 rough voices could only be faintly heard on the command hill.

The Prince was always nervous on the eve of battle. His aides only interrupted his solitary brooding when it was unavoidable. His mind went over all the details of the plan. Like a master chessplayer, he tried to predict every possible move his opponent might make.

But now an officer broke from the semi-circle of staff and approached the general. He carried a sizeable letter from which the imperial seal dangled.

"A fast dispatch rider just brought this, Your Highness. It's from the court in Vienna."

The Prince fingered the heavy paper and then the round seal with the Hapsburg eagle impressed on red wax.

"Just before the decisive battle," he thought. "What game are they playing now in Vienna? Kollonitz's been whispering into the royal ear again."

For a moment he balanced the letter in his slender fingers. Then he thrust it back into the hands of the surprised officer.

"Here, guard it till tomorrow. I'll read it after the battle. Must keep my mind on strategy now."

"But Your Highness—" The officer was horrified. This bordered on mutiny. Men had been summarily shot for lesser offenses.

Helplessly, he squeezed the envelope in his trembling hands. The Prince had turned his back on him and was gazing down at the river. His eyes followed its course until they focused on a narrow wooden bridge. There, on the west bank, glowed the campfires of the Ottoman army, some 100,000 strong. The white circular tents stood ghostly against the purple sky. The strains of weird Oriental music drifted across the plain.

Ant-like swarms of men could be seen throwing up earthworks to protect the bridgehead. The Turkish vanguard had already crossed during the day and was encamped on the east bank. The Prince's sharp eyes could make out a huge tent with a green banner. Kara Mustapha himself was with the vanguard.

The little fieldmarshall bit his lips. Here was his chance. If he could launch a surprise attack while the Turkish army was still divided by the river, the day would be his. Otherwise, in another twenty-four hours, the whole force would be safely across the bridge and out of reach.

His head turned slowly. Now his eyes followed the undulating river upstream. The waters were calm, undisturbed by any vessel.

"Where are the barges?" he fumed. "My artillery's ready, and I've no ammunition. It's maddening."

"Send patrols up the river to see if the barges are coming," he barked at an aide.

"Your Highness, they've been out scouting all afternoon, as you ordered. If they had sighted anything, they'd have reported immediately."

"That confounded Jew." The Prince stomped the ground with his boot, raising a low cloud of dust. "I thought I could trust him. Looked like a human being among all those hyenas at court. But perhaps they're right with their talk about Jews. If he has sold out to Kollonitz—"

There was a commotion among the staff. He swung around and saw a rider who had just dismounted. Standing stiffly at attention, he was reporting to one of the staff officers who then rushed excitedly to the field-marshall.

"Your Highness, the barges have been sighted."

"Sorry, old Samson," muttered the Prince to himself. The officer raised his eyebrows in astonishment. "I did you an injustice. Friends should trust each other. It won't happen again."

Then he snapped into his command voice, "Order two hundred men to the bank immediately. Make it three hundred, even more if necessary. The unloading must begin at once and be finished before daybreak."

Even as the officers scurried about to carry out the orders, the first barge came in sight, hugging the high bank. In the distance, it looked like a floating stick of dark cordwood.

Kara Mustapha, Grand Vizier of His Majesty, the Sultan of the Ottoman Turks and Caliph of all Islam, was asleep in his lavish tent. It was the hour before dawn. A faint light was creeping through the transparent silk curtains.

A stir went through the row of ebony-skinned Sudanese bodyguards who had been napping in a standing position in front of the tent. Then they were wide awake. Pointing into the mist in the direction of the river, they chattered frantically.

The guard officer rushed inside and prostrated himself before the couch that was heaped high with precious rugs and cushions. An instant later Kara Mustapha strode out into the center of the encampment. Officers came running from all directions.

Out of the fog the dull boom of cannons sounded. The noise of many explosions fused into one long, low-pitched growl.

The old campaigner immediately realized what had happened. The little fox of Savoy had outfoxed him once more. And this time, if he lost again, he could expect a messenger from His Majesty in Constantinople with the dreaded silken cord, the Sultan's gracious invitation to hang himself.

Followed by his bodyguards, the Grand Vizier rushed toward the bridge. But he was soon halted by masses of people streaming in his direction.

Day had come, and now the artillery fire from the hills was deadly accurate. Grape and leadballs raked the bridge, which was crammed with horses and wagons and a pushing, frantic multitude on foot. Everybody was desperately trying to reach the safety of the east bank.

Soon the tightly packed mass on the bridge could not move at all. Grape and balls tore bloody holes into it. The wooden structure began to burn. Men screamed, and scared horses leaped over the low railing into the water. Other Austrian batteries were aiming at the encampment on the west bank. In solid sheets, death and fire rained on the doomed army.

His eyes reddened from smoke and his fists clenched in powerless rage, Kara Mustapha watched his glorious army being torn to pieces. It was certain that Allah, the Unfathomable, was not with the green standards of His Prophet today.

Now the Grand Vizier saw the Austrian cavalry charge from the hills. Their red-white-red banners fluttered in the wind. They leaped across the earthworks and through gaps in the hastily formed circle of wagons. There was no fighting spirit left in the frightened hordes of conscripts from the far-flung corners of the Ottoman Empire. In panic, they rushed towards the bridge. When they found it completely blocked, they threw themselves into the river and drowned by the hundreds.

Kara Mustapha had seen enough. The battle was lost. The silken cord would be waiting for him, but still, it was his duty to save the remnant of the army that had crossed on the previous day. At a wave of his hand silver trumpets shrilled out the signal of retreat.

Hours later the barge pilot took Prince Eugene and Samson Wertheimer across the river. The east camp was silent. From time to time, some pitiful figures still broke away from the inferno of the burning bridge. They threw themselves to the ground, begging for mercy.

Silence filled the deserted tents as the victorious fieldmarshall and his purveyor walked slowly along.

Samson shook off the nauseous feeling in the pit of

his stomach. He felt that he had to pay tribute to his friend's great victory.

"The Grand Vizier seems to have left in a hurry," he said. "I'm sure there are plenty of victuals left for a great victory celebration."

The Prince walked on in deep thought. Samson wondered what was bothering him. Finally, the general stopped to stare at a corpse in his path. It was the body of a young soldier, almost a child. He must have been hit by an artillery shell while crossing the bridge and collapsed when he reached the bank. His left shoulder was a bloody mass, and his arm hung from it at a grotesque angle.

"Look at this boy." The Prince's voice was bitter. "Why did I have to cut off his life today? What did he do to me, to any of us? I hate this unending senseless butchery."

Samson could not believe his ears. This was the victorious general, the most famous warrior of Europe.

The same question had been on his own lips, but he had not expected it to come from the aristocrat who walked beside him.

"What a man," he thought.

The Prince walked on. "O, how I long to be back at my palace in Vienna with my paintings and books. I would gladly give away all my victories if I could write like Leibnitz, the great thinker, or like Spinoza, your gentle Dutch philosopher."

The smoke and the acrid smell of burned powder still lingered in the air.

Samson had harbored deep respect for this man since the first time they met. Now he felt something akin to love. He did not know how it came, but all of a sudden before his mind was the picture of his own father in his booklined study, forgetting the world around him as he delved into the thoughts of sages of bygone centuries.

"How did you ever get into this business of financing wars?" The general seemed to have read his thoughts. "Your own people haven't borne arms since Roman times."

"We finance whatever our clients undertake, my Prince. Wars, palaces, schools, theaters. Unfortunately the call is mostly for wars."

"Well, I shouldn't ask. I was the one who wanted you to be my purveyor, and I'm very grateful to you. The ammunition you brought saved the day for Hapsburg's colors."

"Oh, no. It was your genius, my Prince. It was your superb strategy that brought victory today. The Emperor will be pleased."

"The Emperor—that reminds me." The fieldmarshall reached inside his smoke-stained coat and pulled out a rumpled letter. "Colonel Huber couldn't wait to have me read it. He was really worried."

He unfolded it, and as he read his thin mouth broke into a bitter smile.

"Here, look at this."

He thrust the paper into Samson's hands. It was

covered with the fancy curlicues that the scribes of the imperial chancery produced so well:

"—His Imperial Majesty hereby orders Your Highness to refrain from engaging the Sultan's forces in any major battle unless attacked. This will remain in force until you receive further orders. His Majesty counts on your obedience and sends His gracious good wishes.
Bishop Kollonitz,
Chairman of the Imperial Council."

Samson laughed.

"This is the height of irony. When did it arrive?"

"Last evening. I had an idea what it might contain, so I didn't open it. His Eminence, the Chairman of the Imperial Council, can't stand hearing the Viennese cheer my victories."

The purveyor could not suppress a chuckle.

"Now he won't be able to prevent that."

"Who knows what awaits me in Vienna? A triumphal reception or a detachment of the imperial guards to take me to a court martial."

Chapter **8**

The house on Kaerntner Street was uncomfortably quiet. The inhabitants moved about without speaking. Their faces were serious, their eyes wide with anxiety.

Whenever they passed a certain door on the second floor, they tip-toed. Behind that door, in a canopied sickbed, lay the lady of the house, her small white face almost lost in the ruffles and lace of the bedstead.

Downstairs, in the counting room, the clerks stood around whispering. Isaac Arnsteiner, the head book-keeper, was feared as a stern taskmaster. But today he paid no attention to their idleness. He was engrossed in talk with Z'vi ben Menasse.

The former Turkish soldier had become devoted to Samson Wertheimer. He was now his confidential secretary. Only late last night—it was really closer to morning—he had returned with the master from an extended trip.

"Your journey must've been on state affairs of the

first class," remarked Arnsteiner. "Or the Emperor wouldn't have called the master into audience so early in the morning. He had barely time to wash and change clothes. It's all quite mysterious."

"Yes, he was pledged to secrecy, and so was I. But I suppose I can tell you now since it's all over."

"It is? I'm itching with curiosity."

"Samson was sent to Cracow on a most delicate mission. It was good that he still knew his way 'round from his Yeshiva days."

"What was he doing in Cracow? Not much money there. The Polish king is practically a pauper."

"Reb Samson wasn't after money. In fact, he was bringing money to Cracow. His secret mission was to arrange the marriage of Princess Theresia Catharina Lubomirsca with Carl Philip, the Emperor's brother-in-law."

"Our good pious Emperor. When things are really ticklish, he sends his Court Jew. Now the master's become a royal matchmaker too. But what about the money he was bringing?"

"You think the bankrupt Polish throne can scrape together a suitable dowry?"

"So the Jew has to lend the dowry too, or Prince and Princess couldn't get married. What a world."

"Now, Reb Isaac, tell me. What's with the master's wife?"

"Very sick. Frumet's never been a strong woman, you know. Dainty and frail, more like an angel than a human being. Always reading about the Cabbala, always praying

for the coming of the Messiah. Now she's come down
with the fever and it won't leave her. She's often de-
lirious, the poor soul."

The sound of shuffling feet came from the hall.
Arnsteiner opened the door.

"Look, the doctor's leaving, and here is Wolf."

Wolf Wertheimer, a stocky young man in his early
twenties, came rushing into the counting room.

"Come, Z'vi. Mother wants to see you."

The secretary followed his master's son up the carpeted
stairs. From every door anxious eyes peeked, waiting for
news from the sickroom.

Heavy velvet curtains were drawn over the large French
windows. Semi-darkness prevailed.

A thin white hand reached out from under the damask
covers.

"Z'vi, where are you? Come closer so I can see you.
Tell me about the journey. Is my husband coming soon?"

At the foot of the bed stood her children: Isaac, the
oldest, whose fame as a rabbi was already spreading,
Loeb, who with his brother Wolf, was assisting in their
father's complicated enterprises, and Eva, the oldest
daughter.

Z'vi bent over the sick woman.

"The master is with the Emperor, my lady. Leopold
wanted his report immediately, and I'm sure he will be
very pleased. Not only has the master successfully con-
cluded his mission, but in Breslau he engaged a famous
conductor for the imperial orchestra, and you know how
His Majesty loves music. Then, in Leipzig, he redeemed

a string of the most exquisite pearls for the Empress. They had been pawned to pay for the royal trip to Italy. I'm sure Reb Samson will be richly rewarded."

"Is he well?" The words were barely audible. Her breath made a rasping sound. "So much he has on his mind, so many worries. But I've told him often how unimportant all this really is."

"The master is well. But, as you say, he has his worries. Hirschel Meier was seen in Breslau and in Cracow."

"The one who worked for him once?"

"The same. He poses as an independent broker now, but we are sure he is a secret agent for Bishop Kollonitz. Wherever he shows up there's trouble for the houses of Wertheimer and Oppenheimer."

"Jew scheming against Jew. What a shame. Tell me, Z'vi." She tried to raise her head. Tiny beads of perspiration showed on her forehead. "Has Samson visited any of the famous rabbis on his trip? Has he spoken with any of the Cabbalists?"

Z'vi looked up in alarm. Rabbi Isaac signaled him not to upset her feverish mind.

"Yes, he listened to them in the synagogues whenever he could and he promised to pay for the printing of several of their books. And in Breslau he interceded with the magistrates who wanted to expel all Jews who could not pay an enormous special tax. Now they can stay and they're blessing him as their deliverer."

Frumet smiled. Her head sank back into the soft pillow.

"I knew it, I prayed for it. It's beginning to come true. My Samson—a sage, a leader in Israel."

Her eyes were closed, but a smile still flickered on her face.

The door opened and Samson entered.

The members of his family were used to seeing him in his rich court dress, yet now their eyes were wide with surprise. Around his neck lay a heavy chain of pure gold, and suspended from it the double-headed eagle hung, the Hapsburg emblem, also in bright gold.

Loeb stepped close to his father. "What do you have here? I've never seen anybody but a prince wear anything like it."

"The Emperor has given me the chain as a token of his gratefulness. He also gave me his signed portrait."

He pointed at a painting in an oval gold frame which a valet was carrying. He held it gingerly as if it were a live baby.

"What an honor," exclaimed Wolf. "Never has a Jew been honored like this."

"They're honoring my husband, the great leader in Israel," whispered Frumet deliriously. "All Israel is looking up to him, to my Samson."

The Court Factor stepped to the bedside. The others withdrew in silence to the far corners of the room. He pressed a warm hand on her clammy forehead.

"Frumet, my wife. You must get well now. I need you. I love you, my little angel."

"Soon I'll be strong again." Her eyes were on him. Her cheeks took on a hint of color under the tender

caresses of his hand. "Then we'll go down to the Holy
Land together to meet the Messiah."

The hand was withdrawn. His mouth twitched. Only
the rasping of her breath could be heard.

Finally Samson said, "I should stay glued to your bedside, my Frumet. Yet I must hurry away again, but not
for long."

"What is it, father?" asked Loeb, his youngest son.
"You don't have to travel again?"

"No. No journeys till your mother is well. But I must
attend a gala reception at Prince Eugene's house. God
knows I don't feel like feasting now."

"Must you go?" asked Wolf.

"Judge for yourself. It's in honor of the Emperor's
birthday. You know the Prince was almost court-
martialed after the battle on the Theiss. Kollonitz is
still out to ruin him. This is the time when his friends
have to stand by him."

"I think the master ought to go," advised Z'vi. "There's
something in the air, some infernal intrigue. The Bishop's
preparing a blow against his rivals. And that rascal Meier
is in on it somehow. The master's absence would start
rumors of a break with the Prince."

Rabbi Isaac shook his head. "A royal court's worse
than a jungle. The wild animals only devour each other
when they're hungry, but a courtier delights in cutting
his colleague's throat at any time."

"I guess I must go." He cast a last glance at his wife.
She was sleeping now. "I'll slip away as soon as I possibly
can. Z'vi, get me the big leather bag of gold from the

strongbox. It's the reward the Emperor'll give the Prince this evening."

"Which, of course, the Court Factor has to advance."

"Well, that's the way it is." Samson turned to go. "Eva, take good care of your mother. I'll be back soon."

Thousands of white tapers were lighted in Prince Eugene's new palace on Himmelpfort Street. The stream of elegant guests flowed up the broad baroque staircase. The ladies wore giant headgear of gauze and ribbons. Their whalebone-supported petticoats made them look like walking church bells. The gentlemen in their silk and lace garments looked plain beside them.

Vienna's high society was out in full force: archdukes, counts, and a host of lesser nobles, members of the Catholic hierarchy, and a swarm of foreign diplomats who examined everything through their long-handled lorgnettes.

The guests streamed into the huge ballroom. There footmen, silver-candelabras in hand, stood along the tapestry-clad walls. From the vaulted ceilings chubby angels and Greek goddesses painted by the foremost baroque masters greeted the distinguished guests. A string and reed orchestra played light, graceful music in the loggia, which was almost hidden from view by tropical plants.

The Prince, exquisitely dressed, looked even tinier than usual as he greeted his pearl- and diamond-studded guests at the top of the stairs.

"Ah, here you are, Samson. What kept you so long?"

He slipped his arm through that of his former war
purveyor, now the Chief Factor and confidential emissary
of His Majesty. "The gold chain looks good on you. My
very best wishes. You certainly deserve the honor."

They could not stay together for long. The Prince had
to greet new arrivals. Guests crowded around the tired-
looking financier to congratulate him. The ladies smiled
graciously. It was smart to flatter a man who was high
in imperial favor at the moment.

Samson continued to think of his ailing wife. With a
feeling of guilt, almost of shame, he walked through
the ballroom. In a corner stood three men, whispering.
As he approached, they shot meaningful glances at him
and nodded to each other. He recognized Bishop Kollonitz and his former employee, Hirschel Meier. The
third man was dressed in the latest fashion, like a dandy.
Set in a cruel face, his black eyes seemed to mirror the
essence of evil. The Court Factor nodded politely in
their direction without stopping, but they hailed him
with exaggerated friendliness. The Bishop reached for
Samson's hand with an unnatural smile. His voice was
all sweetness.

"My dear Wertheimer, let us add our humble con-
gratulations to the many you are receiving. A great honor
for a fine man, indeed."

"You're still my model," seconded Meier, with oily
humility, "though I no longer have the singular pleasure
of serving you directly."

Samson looked around uneasily. He could almost feel
something slimy creeping up on him. He barely had the

presence of mind to murmur a few polite phrases of
thanks.

"By the way, my dear Court Factor," continued the
Bishop. "I don't believe you've met the Baron von
Edelach. He has recently arrived from Prussia to enter
imperial services and is most anxious to make your
acquaintance."

"I have heard so much about you." The Baron's voice
was high-pitched and thoroughly disagreeable. "Who
hasn't? It will be an honor, Herr Wertheimer, to be at
your service at any time."

Samson conquered a feeling of nausea. Finally the trio
let him move on and resumed their colloquy.

Edelach, Edelach—where had he heard that name
before?

The orchestra struck up a slow-measured minuet. The
gentlemen bowed low in front of the ladies and led
them to the center of the floor. Samson stood next to
one of the rigid footmen and watched the intricate steps
and turns of the dance.

Suddenly he remembered. At the Leipzig Fair, one
of his sub-contractors had warned him that a man named
Edelach would probably appear in Vienna soon. He
was a notorious swindler, whose real name was Nicholas
Peters. He had escaped from many cities, just one step
ahead of the police, leaving behind a trail of unpaid
bills. Several wealthy widows whom he had married were
grieving over their lost dowries. He was a specialist in
swindling considerable sums out of merchants by promising them all sorts of rare goods.

What was this unsavory character doing here in a huddle with Kollonitz and Meier? Something was terribly wrong.

Samson looked around. Everybody who had position or influence at court was here.

But where was Samuel Oppenheimer?

He had not seen his former employer for some time. Perhaps the proud and irascible Oppenheimer was not anxious to talk to his competitor. Samson had edged the older man out of first place as financial advisor and creditor to the throne. The court was often annoyed with Oppenheimer's rather high-handed ways.

But Samuel Oppenheimer was still an important man who held various trusted commissions and tax monopolies from princes and churchmen. It was impossible that he had not been invited. But where was he? It smelled bad.

Samson was about to look for the Prince and ask him. But a burst of fanfares shattered through the hall. The chandeliers tingled. Ladies and gentlemen hastily formed a double row and became frozen in deep bows and curtsies.

Preceded by the pompous master of ceremonies, the imperial couple entered and was conducted by Prince Eugene to a platform with two gilded chairs under a heavy velvet canopy.

The Emperor looked ill at ease, as he always did when a large crowd of his subjects surrounded him. But the Empress radiated charm and happiness, dressed in a flowing gown with a long train carried by a turbaned page. Around her neck hung the newly regained pearl necklace, and on her breast a giant diamond pendant glittered.

Samson made his way hastily through the throng until he stood next to Emperor Leopold. He handed him the heavy bag of gold, and the Emperor in turn presented it to the Prince with a few gracious words about "the glorious victories which our dear Fieldmarshall had won over the vicious Turkish enemy."

Samson moved back and was lost again among the cheering guests. His shoulders were bent as if weighted down by the heavy chain. He posted himself near a door, waiting for a good chance to leave.

Now Their Majesties were seated. The violins and flutes in the loggia played sweetly. All eyes were focused on the stage at the far end of the ballroom.

To the delight of the Emperor, his host had prepared a rare surprise: the performance of an Italian opera.

This new form of entertainment had been only recently introduced to Vienna. Already the Emperor had spent huge sums of money—still owed to his Court Factors—to put on operatic shows. Now, for the first time, somebody outside the royal family was imitating him.

The opera had a complicated plot, involving love, violence, and all sorts of magic. Ancient gods and goddesses appeared from the clouds and disappeared into abysses with the help of intricate stage machinery. In long arias the tenors and male sopranos strained their vocal cords to reach unbelievably high notes.

Leopold I, who was no mean musician himself, knew

the score well. He planned to have the opera played shortly in the imperial palace. After a while he could not contain himself any longer in his gilded seat. During an orchestral interlude, he jumped up and made his way to the loggia where he took the baton from the scared conductor's hand. The Emperor liked to direct orchestras.

Samson heard hardly anything. His mind was back in the sickroom with his wife. He knew the performance would last at least two hours, and then there would be more dancing. The singers strained their voices, but the courtiers kept their eyes glued on the royal conductor. He thoroughly enjoyed their exaggerated applause.

During one such thunder of praise, Samson slipped out of the palace. He roused his dozing coachman and ordered him to drive home.

The streets were dark. He was surprised to see a carriage standing before his house. He had not expected any visitors. Z'vi waited for him at the entrance. With an air of extreme urgency he conducted Samson to the library. Only a lonely candle cast gloomy shadows over the rows of books.

A man sat slumped into a chair. It was Emanuel Oppenheimer.

"Samson, thank God you've come." He sounded desperate.

"What is it? What's happened?"

"They've arrested father."

"Again? Has he been too persistent in collecting his debts?"

"No, no. This is much more serious. Have you ever heard of a Baron von Edelach?"

"I've just met him. Seems to be a most repulsive character. What has he to do with your father?"

"He testified that father had hired him to assassinate you, and Kollonitz ordered his arrest for murder."

"Your father have me assassinated? But that's insane!"

"It's a hellish scheme. Edelach, apparently, will do anything for a price, and Kollonitz will do anything to ruin a Jew. He knew you and father were working against each other as competitors."

"Competition—yes, but murder?"

Now he knew what those three had been discussing. And that was why Samuel Oppenheimer had been absent from the reception. They were already celebrating Oppenheimer's downfall. And then? Who was next on their list?

"Samson, I know you and father have not gotten along too well lately. But you hold his fate in your hands."

"I? It's Kollonitz who had him thrown into prison."

"You must go to the Emperor. It's the only hope. This time they're out for his life."

"And if I stand in Kollonitz's way, it may be my life. Don't forget, he's the president of the Imperial Chancery."

"I know, I—I must leave it to your conscience. Good night."

He rose, a broken man.

As he walked out with halting steps Samson said, "I must go to Frumet now. I will decide before the morning and let you know."

The patient was alone except for her oldest daughter.

"She's sleeping now," whispered Eva, as she motioned her father to a chair.

Samson sat with his head bent and resting on his arms. A flood of thoughts stormed through his weary mind. Slowly the hours of the night crept by.

He saw Frumet's head move, and he bent forward in his chair. Her eyes opened. They were luminous.

She did not see her husband sitting there. But still he was with her in her dream world.

"Samson." The words were barely audible. They came in ecstatic bursts. "Samson, my husband, the Prince of Israel. Together we are walking towards Jerusalem. Our people are following you. They listen to your words, to your teachings about the holy Torah. My Samson, at last you are—"

Her lips continued moving, but no sound came.

Samson turned away. A violent convulsion shook his body. His lips quivered in a soundless sobbing. Eva was frightened. Never before had she seen her father like this.

But it was only for a brief moment. Then he stood up, calm and grim, a man who had just made a vital decision.

He turned again towards the bed. His wife's face was peaceful. All movement had ceased, but a smile still crossed her lips.

Tenderly, he closed her eyelids and drew the covers over the white face that now, more than ever, had the sheen of delicate porcelain.

"The Lord has given," he murmured, "the Lord has taken away. Praised be the name of the Lord."

The heavy curtains hung like sacks of mourning over the windows. He walked over, moved an edge of the velvet material aside and looked out. The rose tint of dawn was filling the sky.

He let the curtain drop again and went to the door where Z'vi was awaiting his master's orders.

"Go, bring Emanuel Oppenheimer. I'll prepare myself immediately to take him to the Emperor."

Chapter 9

Emperor Leopold was having breakfast with his third wife, the young Empress Leonora.

The couple sat alone at a raised table, two small forlorn figures in a cavernous hall filled with courtiers and lackeys dressed in gorgeous vestments. Course after course was brought in from the palace kitchen and passed ceremoniously through twenty-four pairs of hands until the food was finally placed before the royal pair. The Emperor and his wife nibbled listlessly at the meats and pastries.

In the meantime, the ministers were preparing to give their daily reports as soon as Their Majesties were finished with the meal. In whispers, the men of state, with scrolls and sheaves of paper in their arms, exchanged the most recent bits of court gossip.

Suddenly the tedious morning etiquette was interrupted. The dukes and counts surged forward towards the dais. Only the guards along the walls remained immobile.

Samson Wertheimer and Emanuel Oppenheimer had entered. Nobody barred the way of the Imperial Court Factor. Anxiously, the master of ceremonies ran up to ask their business, but Samson brushed him aside without uttering a word.

Hurriedly he strode on. His face was gray with fatigue and grief. His usually well-tended beard hung about his sunken cheeks like an ill-fitting piece of theatrical makeup. A faithful shadow, Emanuel kept close to his heels.

The Court Factor took only enough time for the merest hint of a bow. Then, his voice shaking with anger, he blurted out:

"Your Majesty, is it with your knowledge that a mockery is being made of justice in your capital city?"

Leopold hastily swallowed a bite of roast goose. He half rose in his chair.

"What's the meaning of this extraordinary behavior, Jew? You had better have a good explanation."

Annoyance brought a dull color to the ruler's pale cheeks. An excited murmur filled the hall. The Court Factor could barely hold his indignation in check.

"Forgive my lack of manners, Your Majesty. But my heart's too full to allow for the niceties of speech. The body of my wife is being prepared for burial. I rushed away to warn you that evil men are destroying your fame as the just father of your subjects. Samuel Oppenheimer, your faithful servant of many years, has been arrested under the ridiculous charge of murder."

"Murder—murder." The word went from lip to lip. Then silence fell over the assembly.

"My Jew Oppenheimer a murderer? What tom-foolery's this? Auersbach, what stupid intrigue's being spun here behind my back?"

The hushed group fell away from Baron Auersbach. Standing suddenly alone before his sovereign, the deeply embarrassed Minister of Justice bent a silk-clad knee.

"Your gracious Majesty, Bishop Kollonitz asked for his arrest. I thought it was on your orders."

"Is the Bishop here? Come forward, Your Eminence. You owe me an explanation."

The tall cleric had kept on the outer fringe of the gathering. Now he stepped through a passage of expressionless faces. He wore his dignity like a protective cloak.

"I was going to report to you after your meal, my Emperor." Coldly, he turned to Samson. "You surprise me, Herr Wertheimer. It was for your protection that I found this step necessary. Samuel Oppenheimer had arranged for your assassination. But the would-be assassin thought better of it and confessed to me. Weren't you rather bitter competitors at times?"

He spoke in slow, measured intervals. But the mocking tone did not escape anybody.

"Your Eminence, in our business one has to be cunning to survive. We maneuvered against each other, yes. But murder—you know very well that neither of us is capable of that. A Jew is not a killer. Why, my son Loeb is going to marry one of his daughters."

"We have the sworn testimony—"

"Of a crook. Is it unknown to you, Your Eminence, that the so-called assassin is a widely known swindler and cutthroat? He'll do and say anything if the price is right."

The Bishop was beginning to lose some of his composure. He was about to answer, but the outstretched arm of the Emperor silenced him. The royal couple on the dais had been holding a hurried conversation. Now Leopold spoke:

"Kollonitz, it looks as if you've been fooled. This accusation is sheer nonsense. Yes, yes, Leonora, I'm not forgetting." The Empress had been poking a finger into his rib. "Her Majesty, in her great devotion to our faith, is concerned lest you, a Bishop, might lose respect among our subjects if you are openly proved wrong. We know Oppenheimer's innocent, but he'll stay in prison for a while until this thing blows over. Then he'll be quietly released."

Samson moved forward. He was still a step away from the dais, yet the Emperor involuntarily shrank back a little.

"Your Majesty, you have just agreed that this man who has suffered so much in your service is innocent. Should a guiltless man be kept in the dungeon for even one day? Surely you cannot mean that. It's against the very idea of justice."

A gasp went through the chamber. The courtiers had never heard such audacity.

The Empress pushed an empty plate away. It rang loudly against a crystal goblet. She spoke:

"Jew, you forget yourself. Don't tax our patience too much."

She was pleasantly plump. All over Austria she was known for her great piety. Many thought it was exaggerated.

"Far be it from me to cause you concern, my gracious Empress." Samson's words were clipped. He kept himself under tight control. "Since my ways irritate your wife, my Emperor, will you please release me from your service as of now, and I will leave the city as soon as I have buried my wife."

"Now wait, Samson." Leopold was unhappy. That was too much inconvenience so soon after breakfast. "You can't do that. You know we've done a lot of fine work together."

"Yes, I was honored to be of help, Your Majesty."

"And now we must work together more than ever. Louis of France wants the Spanish crown for his son, whereas it rightly belongs to Our son Charles. Another war is upon us. Prince Eugene is already campaigning in Italy. He has specifically asked that you be his financial adviser. We need you. The treasury is empty. Hardly any taxes are coming in from the provinces. Here, let's not quibble anymore about trifles."

Quickly he scribbled something on a scroll that a chamberlain handed him. "Give me the sealing wax."

The red stick of wax was held over a candle. Big hot blobs fell on the paper. The Emperor pressed the seal from his gold signet ring into them. Then he handed the paper to the Court Factor.

"This will open the prison door. Go, get your man and bring him here. We need both of you."

Samson accepted the paper with a bow.

Before he could voice his thanks, there was a stir behind him. Livid with rage, Bishop Kollonitz stomped forward. He had forgotten all restraint. He stopped to whisper to an aid, who then hurried out. A score of faces were turning in his direction.

The Emperor noticed the commotion.

"Come, come, Bishop," he said good-naturedly. "Don't let this upset you. We can all make mistakes. And now on to more important matters."

"One moment, Your Majesty. In a few seconds I will have something very interesting to show you."

Samson noticed to his surprise the palsied figure of Hirschel Meier limp into the hall with a large bundle of papers clutched under one arm. What was his former bookkeeper doing here in the palace?

The Bishop's face now bore a smile of triumph.

"Allow me, Your Majesty, to present a very good man: Johann Meier, a former Jew, but recently converted to the true religion. Here, Johann, give me the manuscript."

Pride and embarrassment mingled in the convert's grin. The bishop snatched the bundle from his hands and held it out towards the Emperor.

"What I hold here in my hands will rid us of those unbelievers for ever. As soon as I leave here I will arrange to have this manuscript printed. When the people read it they will not rest till the last Jew is driven from your lands, my Emperor, including Herr Oppenheimer and all his friends."

Leopold was curious. For a ruler of the day he was a man of considerable learning. "What is this terrible manuscript you have here. You're clutching it like a battle ax."

"Yes, it is a mighty sword drawn against the infidels. Look at the title, *Judaism Unmasked*. It is the fruit of nineteen years of study by Professor Eisenmenger of Heidelberg. From their own Hebrew writings the professor has collected all their evil teachings—the blasphemies and curses against our religion, the rules on how to destroy Christians. This book will light a fire that will consume the whole race."

The president of the Imperial Chancery cast triumphant glances about him. He was aflame with hatred. By his side stood Meier with downcast eyes, a small misshapen shadow.

Samson had turned to leave. Now he stood greatly alarmed. A new, a frightening danger had suddenly arisen. This was not the first inflammatory book about Jews. He knew what the effect on fanatic mobs could be. And this came at a time when feelings were running high. The other day Samuel Oppenheimer's house had been attacked. There had been looting. Invaluable books, jewelry, and also important business papers had been destroyed. Only the quick intervention of the imperial guard had prevented even greater disaster.

A new incitement to violence could have terrible consequences.

"With Your Majesty's permission." He spoke with restraint. "Will Your Eminence lend me the manuscript for a day? You will understand that I'm interested in the subject. Perhaps I could suggest some corrections."

"I can't see any harm in it, Kollonitz. Let him have the papers. And remember, you may get rid of all the other Jews, but as long as nobody else can handle my finances I need my Court Factors."

"Very well, Herr Wertheimer. Read it to your heart's content. I hope you'll enjoy it. And just in case anything happens to the manuscript, I have a complete copy at my residence. Now, Johann, give the papers to the honorable Court Factor."

Without lifting his eyes, Hirschel Meier took the manuscript from his present master and extended it to his former employer.

The funeral was over.

Through the Wertheimer house many visitors moved, trying to comfort the bereaved family. The mourners sat on low stools listening to the warm words extended to them by Jews and Christians, by Viennese and by others who had hurried to the Danube city at the news of the death.

But the widower was nowhere to be seen.

His heart was heavy with grief. But a voice drove him away from the mourner's stool, and he knew it was the voice of his wife. The dead were in their graves, but the living needed help. Frumet would have wanted him to be a fighter now.

He had shut himself in his study and was poring over Eisenmenger's manuscript. His hands shook with rage as he turned the pages. He had to force himself from tearing the sheets into pieces.

This was sheer poison: the old lies about Jews contaminating the wells to spread plagues, about Christian children murdered in secret rites. The professor had studied the Hebrew scripture and many rabbinic books. But instead of explaining their meaning he had torn sentences from their context and put them together so that they seemed to mock the teachings and sacred objects of Christianity.

The professor claimed to have found secret commandments that ordered Jewish merchants to cheat customers and Jewish physicians to poison patients of other faiths.

Samson thought of his friend Gotthold Regner, the wise Christian thinker. He thought of Baruch Spinoza, the gentle sage of Jewish blood. How could it be that at the same time that those men taught goodness and understanding a learned professor could spread such cruel lies?

Should he write a denial? What good would it do? The mobs would not wait to listen to any denials. Howling with rage, they would fall upon the Jewish quarters.

No, there was only one way to avert tragedy. This book must never appear in print.

The Court Factor had his elbows on the opened manuscript. He buried his graying head in his cupped hands. He could try to wage a battle, the greatest battle of his life. Defeat would mean his end, the end of his family. Should he risk it?

"Frumet," he murmured, pressing his lips against his fingers. "Frumet, my love, will you help me?"

He had disappointed her gravely. But she had never lost hope. In death she had been certain that his efforts would some day turn to worthwhile goals.

He stood up and pushed back the heavy oak chair. He was ready for battle.

During the following weeks the battle raged furiously. Samson had freed himself from all other duties. There was no time for credits and procurements now. His sons and Z'vi ben Menasse had to look after all this.

First he wrote a petition to the Emperor:

"—this evil is threatening not only your faithful subjects, the Jews, but also the whole Empire. Once the mobs are let loose, once order and justice are abandoned to plunderers, the whole civilized society breaks down. Give me a chance to show that those accusations are utterly false. I will prove it through the testimony of the foremost scholars in the Empire, including theologians of your own faith. In the meantime, I implore you to hold off publication of the book—"

Leopold consented to postpone publication for a few weeks. Kollonitz flew into a rage when he heard of it. The battle was on.

Immediately the president of the Imperial Chancery took the offensive. "What a shame," he taunted the Emperor, "if the Jews would have their will in this Christian country. What a spectacle to see them succeed in suppressing the truth."

He urged princes all over the Holy Roman Empire

to add their voices to his. He used his strong influence on the Empress who, in her simple piety, could not imagine that a high churchman could be anything but right.

In the meantime, Samson Wertheimer contacted Catholic and Protestant scholars and the most famous rabbis in Europe. He wrote to scores of professors in many fields. Soon their learned opinions began to arrive at the imperial palace.

A brillant letter came from David Oppenheimer, Chief Rabbi of Prague and nephew of the Viennese Court Factor. The great talmudist, famous for his wealth, as well as for his learning, gave a clear outline of the talmudic literature. He proved very definitely that Eisenmenger's accusations resulted either from complete ignorance or from willful distortion.

Gotthold Regner, now a professor at Berlin, sent a passionate appeal to let reason rather than hate and superstition prevail. Even from the pulpits of many churches and cathedrals sounded admonitions to keep God's commandment, "Love thy neighbor as thyself."

Samson had access to the throne at all times. When he brought the matter up, the Emperor seemed to lean towards his side. He wanted no unrest, no riots. He was now mainly concerned with the War of the Spanish Succession that was raging on many battlefields. It made staggering demands on the Austrian treasury. He needed the advice and the backing of his chief factor.

But Kollonitz tightened his hold on the mind of the

Empress. He told her how it would please God if she helped rid the entire empire of infidels.

The time of the temporary postponement was running out. The decisive moment was near.

Samson requested a private audience with the Empress. She received him early in the morning just as she was returning from mass. As a sign of penitence she and all her ladies-in-waiting were dressed in coarse robes and wore sandals on their naked feet.

The Court Factor bowed, and she extended her hand for his ceremonial kiss. "I have a gift for you," he said.

"Don't speak to me of gold and jewels. I'm doing penance for the sins of our people."

"This gift will please you, my Lady. Here is the deed to a large tract of land for the Carmelite Nuns. And this draft will allow enough funds to build a complete convent for them."

"Wonderful. That has been my heart's desire. I've often implored the Emperor. But you know—the treasury. How did you find out?"

Samson smiled. He had his sources of information just like the other important people around the court. One had to know in order to survive.

The Empress was deeply touched. She thanked Samson cordially, but when he pressed her in regard to the book, she only promised to think it over.

He returned to his house which had become the headquarters of an embattled army.

Couriers came and went. Bodyguards were stationed at the doors, for now real assassins lurked about. The master had had several close calls.

There was spying and counter-spying. Messengers were waylaid and servants bribed. Letters from Samson's learned correspondents had to be smuggled into the imperial palace.

The stay of publication was up today. Soon the printing presses would crank out copies of *Judaism Unmasked*. It was Friday afternoon. Samson had gone to the imperial hunting lodge in Laxenburg and was not back yet.

His study was empty. From it an open door led to a larger room which was in semi-darkness. It had four stained-glass windows which admitted only faint rays of the setting sun.

This was the synagogue of the Wertheimer house, the only Jewish place of worship in Vienna. No other was permitted.

The room was filled. The many house servants, refugees from endangered communities, were there as well as delegations from Worms, Frankfort, and other congregations sent to help prevent the disaster.

The shadows lengthened. The Sabbath was about to begin. The cantor, a coachman during the week, stood by his lectern, but he waited. No sound could be heard, but many lips moved in silent prayer. Several pairs of eyes were glued to the windows though nothing could be seen through the stained glass.

Then they heard the unmistakable noise of a carriage coming to a halt. Some of the younger men, unable to restrain their curiosity, rushed out.

Soon they returned followed by Samson Wertheimer.

The lace and velvet of his court costume contrasted strangely with the somber dark cloaks that the others wore.

The landlord paused at the door.

"What is it, Reb Samson?"

"Speak. Don't torture us."

"Is there hope?"

The impatient shouts were hardly understandable.

"Friends, God has been good to us." Samson sounded very tired, yet a look of triumph gleamed in his eyes. "The Emperor has seen fit to forbid publication of Eisenmenger's book permanently. The manuscript will be kept under lock and key."

A single gasp went through the room. Through the wide open window of the study the first star sparkled. The cantor turned toward the Ark. Jubilantly, he intoned:

"It is good to give thanks to the Lord
And to sing praises to Thy name, O Most High,
To declare Thy loving kindness in the morning,
And Thy faithfulness in the night—"

Chapter 10

Under the pale winter sun that hung over Frankfort-on-the-Main, the city was a riot of color. Every street was draped in banners and bunting. Wooden arches had been erected over the main thoroughfares. They were hung with evergreen and adorned with the Hapsburg emblem, the double-headed eagle.

Stalls covered the marketplace. Men, women, and swarms of children pressed around them to admire here a trained bear, there some midgets, and fire eaters and strongmen who could lift a whole horse. Miracle doctors praised their charms and wonder pills.

In the middle of the plaza there was a large shed, actually only a rough roof made of boards and supported by four posts. Underneath it a whole ox was roasting over a charcoal fire, turning slowly on a giant spit.

Many eyes glanced longingly towards a newly built fountain with two spigots. Later on, at the height of the festivities, one would spout red wine and the other white.

The older burghers remembered similar days, for
Frankfort was the city where, by an old tradition, the
emperors of the Holy Roman Empire were elected and
crowned. The election had become a mere formality,
and the Empire itself, which included Germany, Austria,
and some neighboring land, was only a name. Most German princes considered themselves independent and
would not bow to any emperor.

For centuries the title of Emperor had been given to
the Hapsburg rulers of Austria. It was an honor, a matter
of prestige, not much more.

But the people of Frankfort were not concerned about
the political facts. An election and coronation meant
days full of joy, a glimpse into the fairyland world of
the great who came from all over Europe in their finery.
It also meant a bellyfull of food and drink at somebody
else's expense, and singing and dancing in the streets
throughout the day and night.

This, December twenty-second, 1711, was the coronation day of Charles VI, son of Emperor Leopold I and
brother of Emperor Joseph I who had followed his father
to his death after only six years on the throne.

The windows were packed with curious faces. Young-
sters perched on the eaves of the old houses. The walk-
ways of the city ramparts and turrets were black with
onlookers waiting for the procession to leave the cathedral
after the lengthy coronation ceremony.

A ripple of awe went through the multitude like a
fresh breeze. It became reasonably quiet. The procession
began to form in front of the flag-draped cathedral.

A band of drums and fifes led. Then came a company of burgher militia in black coats, carrying long halberds. Visiting archbishops and princes, ambassadors, and members of the Hapsburg family rode in carriages pulled by two or three pairs of matched horses. The nervous animals were kept in step by front riders and coachmen with long, flower-draped whips. Flanking the carriages were the Swiss guardsmen, disdainfully looking ahead as befitted the most renowned mercenary soldiers of Europe.

Then came the cream of the Austrian officer corps. The uniforms of the various units formed a brilliant symphony of color. Prince Eugene rode in the lead. In red breeches and a flowing blue cloak, the tiny fieldmarshall looked more like the mascot than the leader of the group.

Heads were bared as the cathedral clergy walked by preceded by altar boys carrying golden crosses, holy pictures and censers.

More troops followed, on foot and on horse, with polished brass helmets and flying plumes. Watching eyes were tired by the glittering profusion of color and gold.

The young Emperor approached. Thunderous cheers went up. Handkerchiefs fluttered and caps were thrown into the air.

Chamberlains carried before the sovereign the insignia of his office: the sword, the scepter and the golden orb. He walked alone under a canopy held up by twelve stout councilmen.

The purple mantle bedecked with precious stones hung loose from his shoulders. Its train was carried by two pages. On the Emperor's head rested the crown. Although hastily altered, it was still too large and kept sliding down toward his eyes. It seemed to have been made to fit giants. Charles looked uncomfortable and hot despite the winter chills.

On that day nobody shouted "Hurrah" with more glee than the Jews. They had come from all over the Empire, bringing costly gifts to the new ruler with which to buy peace and protection for another few years.

Nobody knew that their cheers were not meant so much for the monarch under the canopy as for the man who walked behind him. Samson Wertheimer strode along thoughtfully, hardly noticing his friends. He was dressed in black velvet with a gleaming white frilled collar front. The gold chain of honor hung around the neck of the chief factor, who was now serving his third emperor.

The Jews poked each other and pointed at him. "Here he goes." Here went one of them—of the abused, ill-treated—yet he was marching in the procession of the illustrious. With the general cry, "Long live the Emperor," mingled their shouts, "Samson *ha-Nassi*, Samson the Prince." This was a great day for the Jews of the Empire.

More dignitaries rode by, more detachments of soldiers followed. The Jews paid scant attention. And as soon as another corps of drums and fifes marked the end of the procession, they rushed off.

Not one of them was around when the crowd stormed forward to the wine-spouting fountain and to the shed where the roasted ox was being carved into hunks. Nor did they wait for the mounted chamberlains who brought large bags that hung from both sides of their saddles. The riders reached into the bags, and coins cascaded over the cobblestones. Immediately, old and young were scrambling on the ground after the little pieces of silver and copper.

The Jews made their way through the dancing and frolicking throngs to the synagogue. Soon it was filled to the last bench, as on a high holiday. Old acquaintances greeted each other, and there was loud talk across the benches. Then everyone rose respectfully as two elders escorted Samson Wertheimer to a seat of honor by the Ark. Afternoon prayers were said, and Hebrew chants mingled with dance tunes played outside on twirling pipes and screeching fiddles.

The congregation sat expectantly as the prayers ended. Then Rabbi Meir ben Isaac rose. He was the rabbi of Worms, the successor of Samson's father. He enjoyed having such a large audience today:

> "While the new emperor is being hailed by his subjects, we, the Jews of the Empire, want to do honor to our own leader, the great Samson ben Rabbi Isaac, who has done so much for us. He has helped the poor and supported the students. He has saved us from many dangers. We rejoice in the fame and splendor that has come to you, Reb Samson.

Your father of blessed memory would have been
proud could he have seen you walking behind the
Emperor today. You are our spokesman, our *shtadlan*. There have been very few like you since God has
seen fit to disperse His children over the world—"

It was a long, glowing speech. In embarrassment
Samson scratched his left ear. There were vigorous shouts
of approval when Rabbi Meir finally sat down.

Then Samson rose. There was no triumph in his voice.
The congregation was startled by the note of deep
humility that contrasted sharply with his ornate clothes.

"Friends, I do not deserve all this praise. So far I have
only collected unimportant trinkets. I've run after worth-
less goods. I am through with this part of my life."

A murmur of astonishment rose from the benches.

"I have decided to retire immediately and completely
from all my business activities."

The murmur became a roar.

"What's he saying?"

"He must be crazy. Overworked."

"Perhaps the coronation was too much for him."

"Reb Samson, you can't do this. What will become of
us? We depend on you."

"Don't be alarmed, my friends." His arm made a re-
assuring sweep. He knew that many of his correspondents
were in the prayer hall. All of them, family members and
friends, had their financial fate tied to his.

"You have nothing to fear. My sons are old and ex-
perienced enough to look after all those affairs. They will

serve the Emperor and also the archbishops of Trier and
Cologne and all our other clients. They'll—"

"But why? You've been so successful."

"You're the first Jew in the Empire."

"Do you fear your family will share the fate of the
Oppenheimers?"

"No, it isn't that. I know that when Samuel Oppenheimer died his relatives were plunged into bitter bankruptcy. But my sons are well-liked at court. They won't
let this happen. I myself, however, have to turn to more
important work now, work that I've neglected too long.
In this work my father and my wife will be my partners."

Bewilderment showed on many bearded faces.

"What's this? It makes no sense."

"His father? His wife? They're both dead. He's losing
his mind."

"He's getting old. What a shame. Just when he's
climbed so high."

Samson sat down. He had heard the remarks, but he remained silent. Inside him there was peace, and on his
lips a smile danced.

"The master's in the library. Follow me, please." The
servant led the way.

Gotthold Regner had come from Berlin to spend a few
days with his friend. Now since Samson was retired, they
would have plenty of time for leisurely discussion.

The white-haired philosopher entered a room that was
lined to the ceiling with leather-bound books. His friend

sat at a huge desk. Several men stood around. The room
seemed to bristle with activity.

Samson rose to greet the visitor. His beard was gray.
He limped and leaned for support against his secretary.
Z'vi ben Menasse had also aged, but the swarthy Sep-
hardi still walked straight as a reed.

"Welcome, Gotthold. You see what the gout has done
to me. I've been looking forward to your visit. We must
have some good long talks. But first I have to take care of
a few matters. Just look at my books in the meantime. I
know you read Hebrew."

He was back at his desk.

Z'vi bent over him. "Reb Samson, this is Thursday, and
you've not yet prepared your sermon for the Sabbath."

"I know, I know. But look at this desk."

It was piled high with papers, some in single sheets and
others in thick bundles.

"Let me just have a quick look. What is most urgent?
These'll have to wait until after the Sabbath."

He shoved several of the larger bundles out of the
way. They were manuscripts of Jewish scholars who were
asking for his rabbinic approbation.

"Here, this letter. What's it about?"

"From the printers in Frankfort. They're ready to begin
work on the new edition of the Talmud. They want some
advance money."

"Send word to Elkanah Moses, our Frankfort cor-
respondent, to pay the printers. Give me Prince Eugene's
letter that came this morning. I want to read it again at
night when I have more leisure. What else?"

"The delegations. They're waiting. These two people're from Trebitsch in Moravia. You know, their rabbi died recently. They want you to appoint a successor from several candidates. The others are from Aussee. There's been an argument with the town council. They've arrested our elders and threaten to expel the whole congregation. They—"

"That's serious. You men from Trebitsch, be my house guests until I have time to look into your request. You from Aussee, tell me exactly what happened. Looks like it'll need a visit to court—"

Gotthold Regner waited for almost an hour. Finally his host dismissed the worried delegation from Aussee.

The two old men sat under a rose arbor in the garden.

"That's what you call retirement?" Regner was amused. "I had pictured you sitting on this bench all day brooding over some passage in Job or Isaiah."

"I wish I had more time for that. I ought to, for I'm not only the rabbi of Vienna, but also the Chief Rabbi of Austria and Hungary. Many other congregations were kind enough to confer upon me the title of honorary rabbi. It may not mean much, yet I should live up to those honors by tireless studying. But that isn't all."

"I gathered that much. Your library's the busiest place I've seen in a long time."

"Unfortunately, what goes on there is often unpleasant, sometimes tragic. I act as the *shtadlan*, the official Jewish spokesman in the Empire. Upon that library where you sat converge the troubles and tears of Jews from the Rhine to the Vistula. The only real advantage of my former work is that I still have much influence with princes and prelates. In that way I can avert some injustice."

"What a blot on our civilization that such a position is needed." Regner did not flail his arms anymore the way he used to, but his eyes still sent out sparks of hot anger.

Samson shook his head sadly. "If it were not for the commandments of our religion we should long ago have lost our trust in mankind."

"No, Samson, don't say that. All men are not wicked. The human race has not done too well in the past, but it is improving. By little signs, here and there, I can discover the dawn of a better future." He turned and laid a pleading hand on Samson's knee. "My own sovereign, the ruler of Prussia, is welcoming Jews and other oppressed religions to his country. In Holland men of many convictions can speak their mind freely. England is rising from tyranny towards freedom. Slowly, all too slowly perhaps, the power of human reason is growing."

The two old men rose. Arm in arm they walked slowly towards the wrought-iron fence. It was laced with honeysuckle and climbing roses. They looked out into the sleepy side street, empty in the warm sun.

Suddenly noise erupted. Windows opened, and street urchins came running. A strange band of men and women approached. They were pitifully thin, and their clothes hung about them in rags. But their faces were uplifted. In their hollow cheeks burned the fire of a mysterious excitement. With parched lips they were humming a Hebrew song. They came slowly. Some leaned on staffs. A few had to be supported, almost carried.

"What's this?" asked Gotthold. "A pilgrimage? Are there Jewish pilgrims? These people seem to be under some mystic spell."

"I think I know who they are. This old emaciated leader of theirs with the burning eyes—I saw him many years ago. It's Judah Chassid."

He told Gotthold of the Messianic movement which had been stirred up to a consuming heat by Sabbatai Z'vi, the impostor, and which still kept many minds inflamed.

Samson ordered the garden gates opened. The travelers, numbering close to one hundred, slumped down wearily on the lawn. He had food brought, and while they ate and drank he went around talking with them and distributing money. As he had thought, they were on their way to the Holy Land. A few had started out from Poland, and as they marched through the German lands others had joined them. They did not know the distance nor the route to Palestine, but they did not care. God would lead them there, somehow.

Then Judah Chassid rose and gave thanks to the Lord for the food. His voice was hoarse, but it still rang out like a shrill tocsin over the beautiful garden. He signaled with his bony fingers, and his followers got up with groans of pain. His thin white beard fluttered in the breeze as he strode through the gate. With an ecstatic song on their lips, they resumed their journey.

Regner shook his head. He was still looking down the street after the travelers had disappeared around the corner.

"What is it that burns in them? A strange fire. A fierce longing."

"They long for the same goal that your thinkers and wise rulers talk about—freedom, human fulfillment. But for them it is embodied in one place . . . the land of Israel."

Samson looked up to the blue sky. It was as if he could hear his wife's gentle voice. She was calling to him with words of cheer and praise. "Yes, my Frumet," he thought, "I am finally following the road. It is not Judah Chassid's road, but it leads in the same direction."

COVENANT BOOKS

Stories of Jewish men and women to inspire and instruct young people